18 £1-99
M·V

M. K. STAM...

C000085853

Discovering

Maritime
Museums and
Historic Ships

SHIRE PUBLICATIONS LTD

Contents

ACKNOWLEDGEMENTS

I am grateful to all curators and others who have so kindly supplied information and photographs for this book. In particular, I am most grateful to Admiral Sir Patrick Bayly of the Maritime Trust; members of the staff of the National Maritime Museum; Mr A. Osler of Tyne and Wear Museums Service; Mr E. W. Paget-Tomlinson, consultant for Hull Maritime Museum; Mr A. E. Jarvis of the Canal Boat Museum, Ellesmere Port; Mr M. McCaugham of the Ulster Folk and Transport Museum; and Mr A. Browning of Glasgow Museums.

Photographs are acknowledged as follows: Exeter Maritime Museum, plate 8; Hull Town Docks Museum, plate 18; Cadbury Lamb, plates 11-14 and 16-17; Maritime Trust, plates 9 (photograph by Roy J. Westlake) and 10 (photograph by John Miles); Merseyside County Museums, plates 1-7 and 23; National Library, Dublin, plate 15; M. K. Stammers, plate 19; Tyne and Wear Museums and Art Galleries Service, plate 20; Ulster Folk and Transport Museum, plate 22; Waverley Preservation Society Ltd, plate 21.

The cover design by Ron Shaddock shows views of the interior of HMS *Victory* and of HMS *Gannet*.

Copyright © 1978 by M. K. Stammers. First published 1978. No.228 in the 'Discovering' series. ISBN 0 85263 369 6. All rights reserved. No part of this publication may be reproduced or transmitted in any form or by any means, electronic or mechanical, including photocopy, recording, or any information storage and retrieval system, without permission in writing from the publishers, Shire Publications Ltd, Cromwell House, Church Street, Princes Risborough, Aylesbury, Bucks, HP17 9AJ, U. K.

Printed in Great Britain by C. I. Thomas & Sons (Haverfordwest) Ltd, Press Buildings, Merlins Bridge, Haverfordwest, Dyfed.

Introduction

The British Isles have a seafaring tradition that goes back to pre-historic times and the material evidence of this tradition is housed in both local and national museums. The interest in Britain's maritime past is such that maritime museums and preserved ships are an expanding area of the museum world. The variety and location of these establishments is amazing. They range from small local museums set up by groups of enthusiastic local historians — including one in a caravan at Barmouth — to such monumental centres of learned research as the Science Museum and the National Maritime Museum in London. This brief guide is intended to be as comprehensive as possible, although space does not permit more than a brief entry for each collection.

Among the museums listed are many where the maritime exhibits form only a small part of the total collection. A number of historic houses with important marine connections are also included. But this listing of small collections is by no means exhaustive. Many museums hold perhaps one or two fine ship models, often quite out of their local context. For example, Bradford Industrial Museum holds two fine half-models of steam yachts, Huddersfield's Tolson Museum has an excellent builders' model of the steam yacht *Venetia,* while Bury Museum in Greater Manchester contains a large model of a Japanese battleship dating from the turn of the century and St Helens Museum has a fine sailor-made model of the tea clipper *Fiery Cross.* So be prepared to find maritime specimens in museums a long way from the coast!

Most large ports have a maritime collection in their local museum — Glasgow, Newcastle upon Tyne, Sunderland, the Tees, Hull, London, Southampton, Bristol, Cardiff and Liverpool — though some like Liverpool have no special maritime museum building. Such museums are usually financed by local authorities, but an interesting new movement is well under way to set up maritime museums or preserve ships through charitable trusts. These are largely self-financing and dependent on enthusiastic volunteer labour. They are often set up to preserve a specific area or structure or to specialise in a particular type of collection. Probably the two most notable examples of this type of maritime museum are the Exeter Maritime Museum, which is based on an attractive group of warehouses in the old docks at Exeter and specialises in small craft from all over the world, and the Canal Boat Museum at Ellesmere Port, which is also based on an old dock basin and its surrounding buildings and which, after only five years, has the largest collection of inland waterways craft in Europe.

Museums such as these have had considerable success in attracting government grants and labour through the job-creation scheme. It is hoped that the initial impetus will not be lost and that they will be able to develop their collections still further in the future. One of the dangers of museums run by volunteers is the risk of folding up through dwindling enthusiasm or lack of finance. Valuable and historic objects could be lost in this way. However, societies and charitable trusts running museums or preserving ships offer great opportunities for public participation, which the local authority museums find more difficult to do.

There are quite a number of private collections of ship models and other marine objects, but as most are not accessible to the general public they are outside the scope of this book. However, some shipping companies retain the old tradition of displaying pictures or models of their ships, past and present, along with other relics. These often grace the walls of the boardroom or directors' offices, and so viewing them would be a matter of tactful negotiation. The Cunard Line (now part of the Trafalgar House group) had the good idea of using part of their collection of paintings and models to decorate the public rooms of their Cunard International Hotel in London, and further relics of the line's illustrious past are displayed on the liner *Queen Elizabeth II*.

The types of object that have accumulated in the maritime collections of the museums described are many and varied. Broadly speaking one can divide them into five main categories: ship models; ship's fittings; navigational instruments; seafarer's personal possessions and weapons; and shipbuilding and other related craftsmen's tools. In addition there are other types of material evidence which enhance and explain the function of these objects, such as paintings, prints, photographs, tape recordings of ships and seafarers, shipping archives, ship's plans, sea charts and films. But ship models are at the centre of most collections and much of this book will be concerned with them. There are many different types of model and many variations in their accuracy and their finish. The main types may be defined as follows:

Builders' model: completely rigged and finished model made by the builders of the original ship or by professional modelmakers to the builders' order. Common scales for these are 1:48, 1:64 and 1:96.

Constructional model: a hull model with one side left unplanked to show the methods of construction.

Contemporary model: a rigged model, other than a builders' model, made at the same time as the original.

Exhibition model: a model constructed by makers other than shipbuilders for display purposes. Such models are completely rigged and finished.

French prisoner-of-war model: a very skilfully made model, generally of a warship, constructed by French prisoners of war captured during the wars of the eighteenth century and Napoleonic period. Such a model was made from any available material such as bone, and often to very small dimensions.

Half-model: a very numerous type of model, generally from the shipbuilders. Some are fully rigged with a mirror back, while others are hull only. The simplest type of half-model was used to design the lines of the real ship, or to show the method of plating to be adopted.

Hull model: shows only the hull and sometimes the superstructure. Many builders' models are of this type.

Native-made model: a completely finished model made by a native craftsman and an accurate replica of a native type of vessel.

Navy Board model: a warship constructed in the Royal Navy dockyards to the order of the Admiralty. Generally they are hull models, and they display a very high standard of craftsmanship. Their purpose was to show the Admiralty how the projected design of warship would look.

Sailor-made model: constructed by seafarers, often during their off-duty hours at sea, from available materials. Frequently crudely finished but accurate on rigging and deck details even though these may not be to scale. Usually waterline models, sometimes as half-models mounted against a scenic background —'picture models'— and sometimes fitted into bottles.

Votive model: a model made to hang in a church as a thank-offering for safe and successful voyages. Such a model is not really true to scale, but nevertheless possesses accurate details in hull and rigging.

Waterline model: a fully rigged model complete down to the waterline. Such models are often to a very small scale.

Working model: (self-explanatory).

In recent years there has been a movement to preserve full-size craft in addition to the small-scale models. Until about 1960 only the *Cutty Sark* and the *Victory* were preserved as museum ships, and indeed many fine old ships which might well have been saved in later years were sent to the breaker's yard or scuttled. Two examples were the eighteenth-century French sailing battleship *Implacable* and the four-masted barque *Archibald Russell*, almost the last deep-sea sailing vessel built in the British Isles.

The Maritime Trust was set up in 1969 on Prince Philip's initiative to act as a national organisation to restore, look after and put on display ships of historic or technical importance. During its short existence, the Trust has saved many craft that are either unique or the last of their type, ranging from the mid-Victorian naval sloop *Gannet* to the last Tyne wherry, *Elswick II.* The main emphasis has been on the acquisition of craft and the prevention of their deterioration. Nevertheless, many of the Trust's vessels are now restored and open to the public. There are also a number of associated schemes, such as HMS *Belfast* and the Windermere Steamboat Museum, which have been very successful. Nor should one forget the very important rescue of Brunel's steamship *Great Britain* from the Falkland Isles. This vessel was the forerunner of all modern screw-propelled merchant steamers. Many other preservation schemes have been launched both by individuals and charitable trusts. Several established museums have also begun to care for full-size craft, often in cooperation with the Maritime Trust. But ship preservation is very expensive on any vessel, especially if kept afloat, and working condition requires constant maintenance if she is not to deteriorate. As she ages the greater will be the maintenance bill. There are also problems with obtaining materials and skills. Good-quality hardwoods such as oak are expensive and often difficult to obtain. The number of yards with men skilled in repairing wooden boats is declining rapidly. Some museums have set up their own repair facilities in order to retain such skills, while others have commissioned new boats of particular local types and made a complete record of the technique of building them. In so many cases it is not simply a matter of keeping a vessel in good condition, but also one of keeping alive old skills such as building a clinker-built boat or using an adze or sewing a sail. Many individual owners, with much hard work, have rebuilt old craft and brought them back to sailing condition. The splendid fleet of Thames barges on the east coast and the yachts of the Old Gaffers' Association are but two examples. While it is not possible to list every privately preserved craft, I have listed some locations where they can be seen.

There is also another category of historic vessels: those that are not specifically preserved but survive as working craft. This includes quite a number of steam vessels, most of which are port service ships such as dredgers, floating cranes, etc. An interesting new development in this field is the revival of steam towage by the International Towing Company, which is based on the Medway. There are also still many traditional types of small inshore fishing and work boats which are in daily use, for example the cobles of the north-east coast. Apart from the Fal oyster dredgers, the majority work under motor rather than sail. Some types of traditional craft are still being built, sometimes in non-traditional materials such as fibreglass — for example the north Norfolk crab boats; others are the last of their type and could disappear. Many are of ancient origin, such as the canvas-covered basketwork coracles of Wales.

A disturbing trend is the number of sales of old sailing craft to foreign parts, usually for charter work. Perhaps, as in Scandinavia, there should be government restrictions on the export of historic ships such as Thames barges. Other important British ships have been preserved abroad, especially in the United States; for example, the full-rigged ship *Wavertree* is at South Street Museum, New York, and the *Euterpe*, built in the Isle of Man in 1863, is at San Francisco Museum, along with the paddle tug *Eppleton Hall*.

The new discipline of nautical archaeology has led not only to an increased knowledge of types of ship that were previously known only through pictures or written descriptions, but also to their actual recovery. British museums now hold the tangible remains of vessels from prehistoric times onwards. For example, many museums have dugout canoes, some of which are of pre-Roman date; the Museum of London has the Roman Blackfriars barge and County Hall ship, and the National Maritime Museum has the early planked boats from North Ferriby on the Humber and the tenth-century Graveney boat. Even the remains of an early nineteenth-century Sankey Canal flat (barge) recently excavated by Merseyside County Museums are of importance because so little is known about this particular type of craft, although it disappeared within living memory. Other important ancient wrecks are still being investigated, such as the medieval wreck at the Cattewater, Plymouth, and the *Mary Rose* off Portsmouth. Thus the breadth of interest and activity in the field of maritime history and archaeology is very great indeed, and by no means all of it is to be found within the walls of museums. Moreover, most museums have far more objects in store than on display. This guide is basically about what is on public display.

If you have an interest in shipping matters and wish to investigate the holdings of a particular collection, you would be well advised to write to the curator beforehand stating your interest and suggesting a date and time for your visit. Most museums are understaffed or depend on volunteers, and if you arrive without warning to look at the reserve collection, or to carry out some piece of research, the curator may not be available to help you.

Gazetteer

England

BRISTOL
Bristol City Museum, Queens Road (telephone: Bristol 299771)
Open weekdays 10 — 5.30.

This is a small but choice display of models of ships owned or built in the port of Bristol, including Brunel's remarkable passenger ships the *Great Western*, a paddle steamer launched in 1837, and the iron screw steamer *Great Britain*, completed in 1843. They were intended to link Bristol and the Great Western Railway with the United States in an effort to revive the declining prosperity of the port. Bristol's coasting trade is represented by a quayside diorama with some square-rigged trows — the local variety of sailing barge. The star exhibits are undoubtedly the four eighteenth-century warship models built by Hillhouse's shipyard: HMS *Mars*, a 28-gun frigate of 1778; the privateer *Mars*, a privately owned armed vessel for wartime commerce raiding; HMS *Arethusa*, a 38-gun frigate of 1781 with a distinguished battle record in the Napoleonic Wars; and HMS *Melampus*, a 36-gun frigate of 1785. There is also a model of the three-masted steel barque *Favell*, built in Bristol in 1895 by Charles Hill & Company, the successors of Hillhouse's yard. She was the last deep-water sailing ship built at Bristol. She was still sailing commercially until the 1930s under the Finnish flag, and Bristol ship enthusiasts hoped to preserve her. But this was not to be, and she went for scrap in 1934. In the 1960s there was also an unsuccessful attempt to preserve the paddle steamer *Bristol Queen*. Now that the docks at Bristol have closed, the City Corporation hopes to find new recreational uses for them.

The Great Britain, Great Western Dock, Gas Ferry Road (telephone: Bristol 20680)
Open daily, summer 10 — 6, winter 10 — 5.

The most important ship ever built at Bristol does have an assured berth in the Bristol docks. The *Great Britain* was designed by Brunel to run a transatlantic service with his *Great Western*. The original plan was to build a second wooden paddle steamer, but Brunel wanted to build an iron ship, and because no Bristol shipbuilder was willing to attempt such a project the company constructed the vessel themselves in a specially excavated dry-dock. The vessel embodied two revolutionary new developments: she was the first large ship to be built of iron and the first to be screw-propelled. On 19th July 1843 Prince Albert performed the ceremony of floating her out of the dock, naming her the *Great Britain*. There was a long delay between her launching and her trials. It was not until December 1844 that she left Bristol docks — for the first and last time — after suffering great difficulties in squeezing through the locks. She was eventually sent to Liverpool to run a service to New York. On her fifth outward voyage she ran aground in Dundrum Bay on the coast of Ireland. It was eleven months before she could be refloated. Although the strength of her iron hull had saved her from being a total loss, some £22,000 were needed to put her back in commission. As her owners, the Great Western Steamship Company, had already spent heavily on her salvage, they could not afford this, and she was put up for sale. In 1850 Gibbs Bright & Company bought her and converted her to an auxiliary steamer with a large sail area for use on their Australian service. She made over thirty voyages from Liverpool to Melbourne before she was laid up in 1876. In 1882 her engines were removed and she began trading between Liverpool and San Francisco, purely as a sailing ship. Early in 1886 she was badly damaged in a gale off Cape Horn and put into the Falkland Islands for repairs. These were considered too expensive and she became a storage hulk at Port Stanley until she was abandoned in 1937. Her stout hull remained intact and in 1970 she was salvaged and towed back to Bristol on a pontoon; on 19th July she re-entered the dock in which she was built. Her restoration to something approaching her original appearance will be a long and painstaking process. Her bow and stern decorations are well on the way to completion and her new funnel has been erected so that she already begins to look like a ship and not a rusty iron hulk.

CAMBRIDGESHIRE

CAMBRIDGE
Cambridge Museum of Technology, Cheddars Lane (telephone: Cambridge 65330)
Open first Sunday of each month 1— 6.

The fen barge *Black Prince* is being restored, after being excavated from the Ouse near Ely. Fen barges were carvel-built, while the fen lighters were clinker-built. Both types were usually towed in gangs of up to five vessels. The *Black Prince* is believed to be between 100 and 150 years old.

DUXFORD
Imperial War Museum, Duxford Airfield (telephone: Cambridge 833963)
Open daily 11 — 5, or dusk if earlier.

This is mainly a collection of aircraft, which also includes two First World War coastal motorboats, the 70-foot (21.3m) CMB 103 and 40-foot (12.2m) CMB 4. The latter sank the Bolshevik cruiser off Kronstadt in the White Russian campaign of 1919 and won her commander, Lieutenant A. W. S. Agar, the Victoria Cross.

PETERBOROUGH
Peterborough Museum and Art Gallery, Priestgate (telephone: Peterborough 3329)
Open Tuesday to Saturday 12 — 5.

A whole gallery of intricate bone models made by French prisoners interned at Norman Cross during the Napoleonic Wars. One of the best collections of this type of model in Britain.

CHESHIRE
CHESTER
Grosvenor Museum, Grosvenor Street (telephone: Chester 21616)
Open weekdays 10 — 5, Sunday 2 — 5.

The local history gallery includes a massive prehistoric dugout found at Nantwich in 1911 and a model of the local schooner *Enterprise*. The archaeology gallery has relics of the Roman port of Saltney on the Dee.

Also in Chester, the canal basin and Taylor's boatyard, Whipcord Lane, are worth a visit by narrowboat enthusiasts.

ELLESMERE PORT
The Canal Boat Museum (telephone number of Hon. Secretary: 061-980 6223)
Open daily in summer and most weekends.

The largest collection of inland waterways craft in Europe, the museum is entirely run by volunteers.

Ellesmere Port was the canal port of the Shropshire Union Canal, where goods were transhipped from canal boats to sea-going craft and vice-versa. It expanded considerably in the nineteenth century to become an elaborate complex of basins and warehouses, complete with hydraulic pumping stations and a lighthouse to mark the entrance from the river Mersey. Many of the buildings, including the famous Telford warehouses, have been demolished. The museum is housed in the top basin, around the island warehouse which once handled much of the grain traffic of the port. This building is being restored, and so is the adjacent hydraulic pump house, complete with its engines. In summer there are exhibitions of canal equipment, painted ware, etc, in the eighteenth-century toll-office on the opposite side of the basin, and a temporary dry-dock has been built between the locks for repairing the boats.

The collection of boats is extremely varied and includes traditional narrowboats such as the *Friendship* and the Clayton tar boat *Gifford,* and the austere day boats from the Birmingham Canal Navigation. There are also some important examples from the wide canals and these include the 'west country keel' *Ethel* from Yorkshire, two Leeds and Liverpool Canal boats — the 'short' transom-sterned *George* and the 'long' boat *Scorpio* — a Mersey flat, *Mossdale,* built for the Shropshire Union Company as long ago as the 1870s, and a Manchester Ship Canal grain barge, the *Bigmere.* Other exhibits include a weedcutter from the Rochdale Canal, an icebreaker from the Bolton, Bury & Manchester Canal and the graceful diesel tug *Worcester.*

NORTHWICH
Weaver Hall Museum, London Road (telephone: Northwich 41331)
Open weekdays 10 — 5.
   Good coverage of the local salt industry, including transport of salt by flats and Weaver packets, and a salt-crystal ship model.

RUNCORN
The Shaw Museum, Cross Street
Open Tuesday and Thursday 2 — 5, Saturday 10 — 12.
   A small prefabricated building containing a few good photographs of Runcorn in the days of the china-clay schooners, but little else. Old Quay Yard is the Manchester Ship Canal Company's tug depot. The old steamer *Daniel Adamson* is usually moored there. Built in 1903 for the Shropshire Union to serve their Ellesmere Port-Liverpool tug and ferry service, she is now the directors' launch. No public admission, but visible from the surrounding streets and the Runcorn Bridge.

WARRINGTON
Museum and Art Gallery, Bold Street (telephone: Warrington 30550)
Open Monday to Friday 10 — 7, Saturday 10 — 5.
   There is an extensive collection of locally excavated dugout canoes, mostly in store. Other relics of local shipping include a quadrant from a schooner. There is also a model of the Hastings lugger *Albert & Edward.*

CLEVELAND
HARTLEPOOL
Maritime Museum, Northgate (telephone: Hartlepool 68916)
Open weekdays 10 — 5.
   This museum covers the history of the principal maritime activities of the town: fishing, shipbuilding and marine engineering. Displays include reconstructions of the interior of a fisherman's cottage and a ship's bridge and an early example of gas-lit lighthouse lantern complete with lens, from the local Heugh lighthouse.

MIDDLESBROUGH
Captain Cook Birthplace Museum, Stewart Park (telephone: Middlesbrough 37168)
Open Tuesday, Saturday (also Sunday, April to October) 10 — 5.

The original cottage in which James Cook was born has been demolished and the museum is housed in the gatehouse to the park. Its displays illustrate Captain Cook's life and adventures and include many objects that belonged to the famous navigator. A new Cook Museum is planned to celebrate his bicentenary.

REDCAR
The Zetland Museum, King Street (telephone: Redcar 71921)
Open weekdays 10 — 5.30.

The principal exhibit is the *Zetland*, the oldest surviving lifeboat in the world, designed and built by William Greathead in 1800 to the same design as his first lifeboat, the *Original* of 1790. She is clinker-built, 30 feet (9.1m) long with bold sheer and fitted with cork fenders and buoyancy chambers. Her last rescue took place in 1880.

CORNWALL
BUDE
Bude Historical and Folk Exhibition, The Wharf
Open Easter to Spring Bank Holiday, Saturday and Sunday 2 — 5; June and September, daily 2 — 7; July and August, daily 11 to sunset.

Displays on the port of Bude and its canal with exhibits from local wrecks.

CALSTOCK
Cotehele House. 2 miles west of Calstock on west bank of River Tamar (telephone: St Dominick 434)
Open 1st April to 31st October daily 11 — 1, 2 — 6 (or sunset).

The river Tamar sailing barge *Shamrock* is being restored using strictly traditional methods. She was built in 1899 at Plymouth. She was originally rigged as a ketch and was fitted with two drop keels. Later she was fitted with an auxiliary engine and rerigged as a smack. She carried granite chippings until the early 1950s.

FALMOUTH
Barnabas, Softwings and Ellen, moored at Penryn
Visits by arrangement with the Maritime Trust.

The *Barnabas* is a 36-foot (11m) 'mackerel-driver', built at St Ives in 1886 and rigged as a two-masted lugger and the last survivor of the great Cornish sailing fishing fleet.

The *Softwings* is a 24-foot (7.3m) cutter, built at Penpol in 1910 for dredging oysters in the river Fal. The *Ellen* is a 17-foot (5.2m) crab boat, built at Penryn in 1882.

Maritime Museum, Royal Cornwall Polytechnic, Church Street
Open Monday to Friday 9.30 — 12.30, 2 — 5; Saturday 9 — 12.30.

The principal exhibits are concerned with the Post Office sailing packets that used to sail from Falmouth; there is a fine model of the packet *Crane* of 1842.

PENZANCE
Museum of Nautical Art
Open March to September 10 — 1 and 2 — 4.

An extensive collection of objects gathered from local wrecks, including many items from Sir Cloudesley Shovel's squadron, which was wrecked on the Scillies.

ST MICHAEL'S MOUNT
Open, summer on Monday to Wednesday and Friday, 10.45 — 4.45; winter on Monday, Wednesday and Friday by appointment.

This spectacular sea fortress contains two graceful rowing barges belonging to its owners, the Lords St Levan. Both date from the nineteenth century and were used as ferryboats to and from the mainland.

TRESCO
Valhalla Museum, Tresco Abbey (telephone: Scillonia 876)
Open weekdays 10 — 4.

This is a unique collection of figureheads and decorations from ships wrecked on the treacherous rocks around the Scillies, including the tea clipper *Friar Tuck*, the SS *Serica* of 1888 and the *Alesandro Il Grande*, an Austrian brig of 1851.

TRURO
County Museum and Art Gallery, River Street (telephone: Truro 2205)
Open November to March 10 — 4, April to October 10 — 5.

The museum holds on long-term loan important items from the *Santo Christo de Castello*, a Genoese merchantman wrecked near Mullion Cove in 1666.

CUMBRIA
BARROW-IN-FURNESS
Barrow-in-Furness Museum, Ramsden Square (telephone: Barrow-in-Furness 20650)
Open weekdays 10 — 7.

Displays include the history of the port and the local shipbuilding works of Vickers Limited. There is a beautifully detailed model of the Dreadnought-type battleship *Erin* launched by Vickers in 1913 for the Turkish navy and taken over by the Admiralty at the outbreak of the First World War.

More models of Vickers ships are visible in the foyer of their training school in the town centre, close to the main bridge.

Barrow is also a centre for old sailing boats; at the Ferry beach on the east side of the Walney Channel, next to the building berths, there is a splendid clutter of workshops, boatsheds and boats. Among the most interesting are the *White Rose*, a fine-lined Victorian yacht designed and built at Barrow in 1887 and still winning races, and the *Gladys*, one of the last Isle of Man fishing nobbies.

CONISTON
Coniston steam launch Gondola, beached near Nibthwaite

The *Gondola* was built in 1859 at Liverpool — in prefabricated iron sections which were assembled at the lakeside. She ran regular trips on the lake until 1939 and carried many famous people, including Carlyle and Ruskin. The latter, who normally hated anything powered by steam, took a great interest in this elegant little steamer. After the Second World War she was converted to a houseboat and her engines were removed. Her present owner hopes eventually to restore her. There is also a model of her in the Coniston Museum.

MARYPORT
Maritime Museum, 1 Shipping Brow, Senhouse Street (telephone: Maryport 22501)
Open Tuesday to Saturday 10 — 12, 2 — 4.

This small museum depicts the history of this once prosperous port. In the nineteenth century Maryport was a major coal port for the export of coal and iron and a shipbuilding centre. The extensive docks are now derelict and used only by a few fishing boats. The remains of Ritson's shipyard can be seen on the banks of the narrow river Ellen, close to the museum.

MILLOM

The *Harriet*, the last Fleetwood sailing trawler, built about 1890, is beached here for conversion to a seaside home.

WHITEHAVEN
Public Library and Museum, Lowther Street
Museum open during library hours.

The museum holds a collection of local shipping material which it is hoped to display in a separate maritime museum.

WINDERMERE
Windermere Steamboat Museum, Rayrigg Road, Bowness (telephone: Windermere 2117)
Open weekdays April to October (inclusive) 10 — 5, Sunday 2 — 5.

A unique collection of Lakeland steam launches and boats, salvaged and restored by Mr G. Pattison, is housed in a new covered dock and exhibition hall.

The earliest complete boat is a clinker-built lug-rigged sailing boat of about 1780, discovered whilst serving as a chicken-house at Southport. Salvaged after sixty years on the bed of Ullswater the steam launch *Dolly* is listed in the *Guinness Book of Records* as the oldest mechanically powered boat in the world. She is driven by her original machinery and none of her hull timbers has had to be replaced. The *Esperance* was built in 1869 for the Furness industrialist H. W. Schneider, who used her for commuting from his mansion to the railway station. She is also known as Captain Flint's houseboat in Arthur Ransome's *Swallows and Amazons*. She was salvaged from the lake in 1941. The *Raven* of 1871 was the Furness Railway's cargo ship on Windermere and carried all kinds of goods to and from settlements around the lake before the building of modern roads. The steam launch *Bat* was built in 1891 by the famous local boatbuilder, Brockbanks. In 1904 she was successfully steered round part of the lake during an early experiment in radio control. The *Branksome* of 1896 represents the ultimate in elegance. She has both a cabin and an open canopy abaft the engines and boiler. Her cabin is richly furnished with embossed velvet upholstery, marble hand wash-basin, etc. Her steam tea-urn boils a gallon (4.546 litres) of water in ten seconds! The *Otto*, which was built in the same year, is a complete contrast to the *Branksome;* she has a sleek steel hull, 43 feet (13.1m) long by only 6 feet (1.8m) beam, built for speed. She is capable of 18 miles per hour (29km/hour). Representing the change to internal combustion engines for powering open boats are an early motorboat of 1898, salvaged from a compost heap in 1955, and the speedboat *Canfly* of 1922. She is powered by a six-cylinder Rolls-Royce Hawk engine of 1917 from the Royal Naval airship SST3. For many years she was the fastest boat on the lake with a top speed of 30 miles per hour (48.3km/hour).

Other boats on show include the steam launches *Lady Elizabeth* of 1895 and *Swallow* of 1911, Beatrix Potter's rowing boat from the tarn above her home in Sawrey and a portion of a clinker-built boat of about 1735.

DEVON

APPLEDORE
North Devon Maritime Museum, Odun House, Odun Road (telephone: Bideford 6211)
Open Easter to 30th September daily 2.30 — 5.30, and 11 — 1 Tuesday to Friday.

The seaport village of Appledore has long had associations with the famous West Country schooners. The museum houses exhibitions on most aspects of North Devon's maritime history. Displays include models, photographs and paintings on such topics as sea trades, shipbuilding, fishing, river and coastal craft, pilotage and navigation.

The North Devon Museum Trust, which runs this museum, also owns the local sailing barge *JJRP*. She is moored in the river awaiting restoration and is not open to the public. Built in 1923, she was the last of the local fleet of open-hold barges employed in collecting sand and gravel from the banks of the Taw and Torridge estuary to be built for sailing. She is 37 feet (11.3m) long, 13 feet (4.0m) in beam and 5 feet 4 inches (1.53m) in the hold. She can load 27 tons (27.4t). In 1925 she was fitted with a 10-horsepower (7.5kW) single-cylinder Widdop semi-diesel engine, which she still retains. She was laid up in 1961 and was later sunk at Bideford.

BARNSTAPLE
Arlington Court, 7 miles north-east of Barnstaple on A39 (telephone: Shirwell 296)
Open 1st April to 31st October 11 — 1, 2 — 6.

This Regency house, the ancestral home of the Chichester family, contains a fine collection of thirty-six French prisoner-of-war models in bone, ivory and wood and also models of the various types of little ship that went to Dunkirk in 1940, together with models in glass, bronze and silver, including one of Sir Francis Chichester's *Gipsy Moth IV*. There are also many sailor-made models. This splendidly assorted collection was assembled by the late Miss Rosalie Chichester between 1908 and 1949.

BIDEFORD
Bideford Museum, Municipal Buildings (telephone: Bideford 486)
Open Monday to Friday 10 — 5, Saturday 10 — 12.45.

The collection includes local shipwright's tools.

BRIXHAM
Brixham History Society Museum (overlooking the harbour)
Open mid May to end of September 10 — 1, 2.30 — 5, 7.15 — 9; winter months, Wednesday and Friday 2.30 — 5.

The upper floors of the group of old buildings which constitute the museum are devoted not only to the history of Brixham and its famous fleet of sailing trawlers, but also to the work of the coastguard service. There is an extensive range of lifesaving equipment and a display showing some of the ingenious methods used by eighteenth-century smugglers to conceal their contraband from the coastguards. There are also displays of the tools and equipment of the shipwright, the sailmaker, the blockmaker, the sparmaker, the rigger and the pumpmaker.

DARTMOUTH
Maritime Museum, Butterwalk, Duke Street
Open May to September, weekdays 11 — 5, Sunday 2 — 4.

A worldwide selection of ship models, especially notable for its excellent glass ships. The privately preserved steam tug *Portway,* which will be given to the Maritime Trust in due course, is also kept on the river Dart.

EXETER
Exeter Maritime Museum, The Quay (telephone: Exeter 58075)
Open daily 10 — 5 (June to September 10 — 6).

Sponsored by the International Sailing Craft Association, this is the world's biggest collection of working boats with over eighty craft displayed afloat, ashore and under cover. Since 1969 the museum has grown to occupy two groups of warehouses on either side of the river, together with much of the quay space of the old port of Exeter. It is a striking example of the reuse of an obsolete dock area for museum display. The two parts of the museum are connected by ferryboat. There are also rowing boats for hire and river trips to Double Locks in the Edwardian launch *Lady Betty.*

Starting at the canal basin entrance, the visitor will be confronted by the massive steam tug *St Canute,* the largest of all the exhibits. She was built in Scandinavia in the 1930s and was later used in the port of Falmouth. Visitors are usually allowed on board. Close by lie the Fal oyster dredger *Sunny South* and the former Bristol Channel pilot cutter *Cariad.* This type was noted for its sea-keeping qualities because the cutters often used to stay at sea in all weathers in the gale-torn Bristol Channel seeking incoming ships that required pilots. She is to be joined by another former pilot cutter, the French *Jolie Brise* of 1913, latterly a Portuguese yacht. The modern yacht *Cheers* is a complete contrast in design, being built along the lines of a twin-hulled proa of the Pacific islands. She finished third in the single-handed transatlantic yacht race in 1968. The *Bertha* is a dredger fitted with a large lowering spoon or paddle to clear mud from the quaysides at Bridgwater. She was designed by Brunel and built in 1844. A similar vessel also operated at Bristol. Here also are a beautiful pearling dhow from Bahrain in the Persian Gulf and three of the Ellerman collection of Portuguese boats, including a spectacular xavega — a 55-foot (16.8m) beachboat worked by a crew of twenty with four large oars and believed to be of very ancient design, used for seine netting — and a Tagus lighter, which is kept afloat. The adjacent two-storey warehouses contain a number of full-size open boats, including two small dhows from Dubai and Bahrain and a bartinha, a raft-like craft made of palm fronds, which also comes from the Persian Gulf. There are also models of craft not represented in the collection, including a Chinese junk and two types of Cornish fishing lugger.

The group of warehouses on the opposite bank contains a wide diversity of small open boats. There are two Dutch dinghies and a collection of rowing boats used for deep-sea voyages, including *Britannia*, in which John Fairfax became the first man to row the Atlantic alone, *Britannia II*, in which John Fairfax and Sylvia Cook crossed the Pacific, and *Supersilver*, in which Tom McLean rowed the Atlantic in record time in 1969. Some boats from the West Country are also exhibited here. They include four different types of fishing boat from Devon, a tub boat from the Bude Canal fitted with wheels for haulage on the inclined planes of the canal, and the *Cygnet*, a most eccentric craft, built in the form of a swan. She was the tender to a larger swan-shaped yacht called the *Swan* that sailed for many years in the Exe estuary. The two out-stretched wings acted as sails. A group of three Mediterranean work boats complete this section: a dghaisa or harbour ferry; a kajjik fishing boat from Malta; and a Venetian gondola. There is also a foyboat, a coble from the Tyne used for moving mooring warps and ferrying pilots to their ships.

The remainder of the Ellerman collection of six Portuguese boats is housed in the adjoining warehouse. These include a netinha, an extinct type of beach fishing boat once found north of Lisbon, a valboeiro from the river Douro and a raboa, a small wine boat from the Douro. The two Douro boats are clinker-built and possibly of Viking descent.

ILFRACOMBE
Ilfracombe Museum, Wilder Road
Open weekdays, 10 — 5.

Ship models are on display and a good collection of photographs is held in store.

KINGSWEAR

The paddle steamer *Compton Castle*, a retired river Dart excursion steamer, converted into a floating restaurant, was up for sale at the time of writing.

MORWELLHAM
Morwellham Quay, near Tavistock (telephone: Gunnislake 832766)
Open daily, summer 10 — 7, winter 10 — dusk.

A historic river port on the Devon side of the Tamar, with remains of nineteenth-century quays, waterwheels and inclined planes linking the port with the copper and arsenic mines it served. An audio-visual introduction to its history is available and there are self-guided trails round the site. Little sailing vessels like the *Shamrock* at Cotehele once sailed from here.

PLYMOUTH
City Museum and Art Gallery, Drake Circus (telephone: Plymouth 68000)
Open weekdays 10 — 6 (Friday 10 — 8), Sunday 3 — 5.

A good collection of marine paintings by artists connected with Plymouth, such as Nicholas Condy, Butterworth and Captain R. B. Beechey. The museum also possesses the Harmsworth collection of sea pictures and ship models, most of which are displayed at Buckland Abbey, Yelverton.

Dockyard Museum, Devonport
Between the beginning of April and the end of September there are free conducted tours of the dockyard on foot lasting one and a half hours, including a visit to the museum. Tours start at 9, 11, 2 and 4 on Tuesdays, Wednesdays and Thursdays, except public holidays, starting at the Granby Gate.

Kathleen and May, Guys Quay, Sutton Harbour (telephone: Plymouth 68943)
Open daily Easter to October, 11 — 6.

The *Kathleen and May* is a wooden three-masted topsail schooner fully restored by the Maritime Trust as one of the last examples of a type of vessel that was once commonly found in the coasting trade. She was built at Connah's Quay on the North Wales coast in 1900 for local owners who insisted on the best timber and materials. She was later sold to West Country owners and in due course she was fitted with an auxiliary diesel engine and her rig was reduced. She continued as a commercial trader until the 1960s. On board there is an exhibition about schooners and their trades. She may move to St Katharine's Yacht Haven, London, in the near future.

SALCOMBE
Sharpitor, 1½ miles south-west of Salcombe
Open April to October daily 11 — 1, 2 — 6.

The museum is housed in part of a property cared for by the National Trust, overlooking Salcombe Bay. It has displays on local ships and shipbuilding. Salcombe was famous in the nineteenth century for its fast schooners sailing in the fruit trade.

Island Cruising Club, Island Street
The club runs an extensive range of sailing courses and holidays in dinghies and yachts. Among their yachts are the old two-masted schooner *Hoshi,* built by Camper & Nicholson in 1908, Sir Alec Rose's *Lively Lady* and the converted Brixham trawler *Provident,* also ketch-rigged and on loan from the Maritime Trust.

19

TOPSHAM
The Topsham Museum, 25 Strand Street
Open Mondays, Wednesdays and Saturdays 2 — 5.

Topsham is a pleasant suburb of Exeter and was once a separate port. On the upper floors of a charming old house Topsham's history is revealed, and there are a sail loft, shipwright's tools and photographs.

YELVERTON
Buckland Abbey (telephone: Yelverton 3607)
Open Easter to 30th September, weekdays 11 — 6, Sunday 2 — 6; October to Easter, Wednesday, Saturday and Sunday 3 — 5.

A thirteenth-century Cistercian monastery converted to a dwelling at the Dissolution, Buckland Abbey was later owned by the distinguished Elizabethan seafarer Sir Richard Grenville. However, Sir Francis Drake was its most famous owner — the best-known of all the Elizabethan navigators, also renowned for his naval campaigns against the Spanish. The house contains relics of Drake, including his famous drum, and the Harmsworth collection of ship models including sailor-made and French prisoner-of-war models.

DORSET
BOURNEMOUTH
Rothesay Museum, 8 Bath Road (telephone: Bournemouth 21009)
Open April to October, weekdays 10 — 6; November to March, weekdays 10 — 5; Sunday 2.30 — 5 all the year.

Ship models are among the exhibits in the marine rooms of this museum.

POOLE
Maritime Museum, Paradise Street (telephone: Poole 5323)
Fourteenth-century vaulted cellars provide an atmospheric backdrop to this new museum whose theme is the history of the port from prehistoric times, through its medieval prosperity, to the early twentieth century. Full-size local boats on show include an X Class yacht of 1909 and a National 14 dinghy.

EAST SUSSEX
EASTBOURNE
Royal National Lifeboat Institution Museum, Grand Parade (telephone: Eastbourne 4717)
Open daily 9.30 — 5 (winter 9 — 1).

Displays illustrate the development of lifeboats and lifesaving techniques from the earliest date to the present day.

HASTINGS
The Fisherman's Museum, Rock a Nore (telephone: Hastings 1952)
Open April to September 10 — 6.

The largest exhibit is a full-size Hastings two-masted sailing lugger built in 1909. This type of fishing boat, now fitted with an engine, is still worked from the beach at Hastings. It has a distinctive clinker-built hull with an unusually broad beam and is among the largest of the beach boats of the British Isles.

Museum of Local History, Old Town Hall, High Street.
Open Easter to mid October, weekdays 10 — 12.30, 1.30 — 5.30.

Displays include objects associated with the history of the Cinque Ports and local maritime history. There is a model of a Dutch East Indiaman similar to the *Amsterdam*, whose wreck off Hastings is one of the biggest archaeological finds in recent years. Her hull appears to be intact and contains a rich variety of ship's equipment, cargo and personal possessions. When funds permit it is hoped to recover the vessel and her contents.

ESSEX
The creeks and little harbours of this county are one of the busiest areas for the preservation of small sailing ships in Britain. The spritsail Thames barges, the oyster-dredging smacks and the shrimping bawleys were all built here and examples of each type have been rescued, lovingly restored and kept in sailing condition. One of the best centres is the little town of Maldon, which still supports an old-fashioned boatyard where many of the Thames barges are repaired. It is possible to arrange trips on the barges and enquiries should be addressed to the East Anglian Tourist Board, 14 Museum Street, Ipswich, Suffolk.

COLCHESTER
Colchester and Essex Museum, The Castle (telephone: Colchester 77475)
The town has a fine museum in the Castle. It is mainly devoted to Colchester's Roman past, but there are paintings and models of barges in its reserve collections.

SOUTHEND
Prittlewell Priory Museum, Priory Park (telephone: Southend-on-Sea 42878)
Open April to September weekdays 10.30 — 5.30, Sunday 2.30 — 6; October to March 10.30 — 4 (weekdays only).

A local history museum containing a model of a fishing bawley from the district and other ship models, including one of a tea clipper.

GREATER LONDON

CAMDEN
British Museum, Great Russell Street, WC1 (telephone: 01-636 1555)
Open weekdays 10 — 5, Sunday 2 — 6.

The treasures of this national museum include the finds from the famous Sutton Hoo ship burial.

CITY OF LONDON
Museum of London, London Wall, EC2 (telephone: 01-600 3699)
Open Tuesday to Saturday 10 — 6, Sunday 2 — 6.

A new museum formed from the collections of the former London and Guildhall museums. The new exhibitions illustrate the social history of London from prehistoric times to the present, and of particular interest to the marine-minded visitor are the remains of two Roman vessels, one discovered on the site of County Hall in 1910 and the second found between Blackfriars Bridge and the nearby railway bridge in September 1962. A mechanical excavator brought up the fragments of oak planking which was discovered to be from an ancient boat. A coffer dam was erected to allow full excavation of the wreck. Archaeologists have since found that the vessel was a 50 to 55 foot (15-17m) river barge with an almost flat bottom, a single square sail and a central cargo hold. The vessel, known as the Blackfriars barge, has been dated to the second century AD, during the Roman occupation of Britain. However, her style of construction belongs to an earlier Celtic tradition. She is the earliest sailing vessel found in north-west Europe. Fragments of pottery, parts of several pairs of Roman shoes, a piece of a leather bag decorated with a dolphin design and other relics have been recovered.

The museum's staff are also involved in other nautical archaeological projects including the search for the remains of Drake's *Golden Hind*, which was preserved at Deptford for a number of years after his famous circumnavigation of the world.

GREENWICH
Cutty Sark and Gipsy Moth, King William Walk, Greenwich, SE10 (telephone: 01-730 0096)
Open weekdays 11 — 6 (summer), 11 — 5 (winter), Sunday and Boxing Day opens at 2.30.

The last and most famous of the tea clippers is now in a permanent dry berth overlooking the Thames, fully rigged just as she would have been in her sea-going days. The *Cutty Sark* was built at Dumbarton on the Clyde in 1869 by two young men, William Dundas Scott-Monterieff, a civil engineer, and Hercules Linton, a naval architect. Captain John Willis, her owner, wanted a ship that would beat the clipper *Thermopylae,* recently launched at Aberdeen. The ship that the two partners built for him was of composite construction — a combination of iron frames and wooden planking — and 212 feet (64.6m) in length and 36 feet (11.0m) in the beam, with a gross tonnage of 963 (978.4t). Their price for the job proved to be low, and after completion they went into voluntary liquidation. However, the *Cutty Sark* was constructed of the finest materials and her survival is a testimony to the excellent workmanship of her builders.

The *Cutty Sark,* in a sense, came after her time, for the opening of the Suez Canal in 1869 gave a decisive advantage to the steamers in the China trade. She managed to find cargoes of tea until 1877 and after that she sailed mainly in the London-Australia trade, carrying general cargoes to Australian ports such as Sydney or Melbourne and returning with bales of wool. Her best performances were under Captain Woodget, who commanded her between 1885 and 1895. In the latter year her owner sold her to the Portuguese because he could no longer make her pay. She was renamed the *Ferreira* and traded under the Portuguese flag for over twenty years. After she was dismasted off the Cape of Good Hope in 1916 she was towed into Cape Town and rerigged as a barquentine. Her hull was as sound as ever but her Portuguese owners found it increasingly difficult to find cargoes for her. On a rough day in 1922 she sought refuge at Falmouth, where she was recognised as the old clipper by a retired seafarer, Captain Wilfrid Dowman. Dowman, who ran a local sea training scheme for boys, succeeded in buying her back and restored her original rig. He used her as a moored training ship at Falmouth until his death in 1937. She was then towed to the Thames where she acted as a training ship for HMS *Worcester,* and fortunately she escaped any damage during the wartime blitz. In the early 1950s she was handed to a preservation society formed on the initiative of Prince Philip and the Director of the National Maritime Museum. The long and exacting task of restoring her to her 1870s appearance was completed in 1957, when she was opened to the public by the Queen. Although she is now in dry-dock she still retains much of the atmosphere of her sea-going days. Her hold and 'tween-decks have been converted to exhibition spaces.

Gipsy Moth IV was the ketch in which Sir Francis Chichester made his single-handed passage round the world in 1966.

National Maritime Museum, Romney Road, SE10 (telephone: 01-858 4422)
Open (summer) weekdays 10 — 6, Sunday 2.30 — 6; (winter) Monday to Friday 10 — 5, Saturday 10 — 4, Sunday 2.30 — 5.

The National Maritime Museum is the national museum which illustrates and preserves the maritime history of Britain. It covers the history of the Royal Navy, the Merchant Navy, fishing, yachting, navigation and astronomy, nautical archaeology, lifesaving, lighthouses and port services.

The museum stands in Greenwich Park, occupying two distinct groups of buildings: the Main Buildings, and the Old Royal Observatory, some ten minutes walk up the hill across the park. The Main Buildings and the Royal Naval College (designed by Christopher Wren),on the opposite side of Romney Road, stand on the site of a Tudor royal palace, and together they constitute one of the finest groups of buildings in London. In the centre of the Main Buildings is the Queen's House, a small palace designed by Inigo Jones for James I's queen, Anne. It was started in 1616 and was not completed until 1635; it was the first building in the Palladian style in England. Although it has suffered great changes inside and out, nevertheless it is a delightful building, which makes a fine centrepiece for this great museum. It is linked by colonnades to the east and west wings, which were built at the beginning of the nineteenth century. Attached to the west wing is a large glass-roofed hall — the New Neptune Hall — erected in Victorian times.

The Old Royal Observatory consists of six buildings. The most important are Flamsteed House, built in the late seventeenth century as the home of the first Astronomer Royal, the first observatory, of the same date, and the Meridian Building, which is mainly of the eighteenth century. The South Building, of late Victorian date, houses the museum's planetarium.

The museum's collections are as distinguished as its architecture. Only a proportion are on display and there are extensive reserve collections. In addition there is a library covering most maritime subjects and a huge collection of ship's plans and photographs, together with a fine archive of naval documents. The museum is also rapidly expanding its collection of merchant shipping records. Some of these collections of books, plans and photographs have been published. Anyone wishing to make use of the museum's research facilities should, wherever possible, write to or telephone the museum at least a week in advance of their visit. Regular users of the library may apply for a reader's ticket.

The main entrance to the Main Buildings lies at the east wing. This building contains displays about British shipping in the nineteenth and early twentieth centuries, the high point of British sea power. Subjects covered include the nineteenth-century emigration traffic from England to North America, wooden coastal sailing vessels, the development of steamships in the late nineteenth and early twentieth centuries, and fishing vessels. On the first floor there are galleries devoted to nineteenth-century marine paintings, the Navy of Victorian times, and the Royal and Merchant Navies in the two world wars.

From the east wing the colonnade leads to the Queen's House, which is furnished in seventeenth-century style. The great hall is used from time to time for temporary exhibitions while the other staterooms house some of the greatest treasures of the museum, including the paintings of the finest of the Dutch seventeenth-century marine artists, the Van de Veldes (father and son), seventeenth-century navigational instruments and over a dozen Navy Board models of seventeenth-century warships.

The west wing contains the library, study rooms and eight galleries devoted to the history of the Royal Navy from 1688 to 1815. These contain more very fine Navy Board models and naval portraits. Of particular interest are the many relics of Admiral Lord Nelson, including his vice-admiral's uniform coat, which he was wearing on 21st October 1805 when he was fatally wounded by a French sniper during the battle of Trafalgar. At the south end of the west wing there is a display on the history of navigation which contains four more of the museum's greatest treasures — the four timekeepers or chronometers made by John Harrison between 1736 and 1761. These were so accurate as to enable navigators to determine their longitude exactly for the first time. Another annexe houses a special exhibitions gallery. The New Neptune Hall contains the museum's largest exhibit — the almost complete hull of the paddle tug *Reliant* built in 1907 at South Shields for work on the Manchester Ship Canal. She worked in her later career at Seaham on the north-east coast. Part of her stern and one paddle wheel have been removed to make space for other displays, but all her essential features remain. The *Reliant*'s unique side lever engines — of a type similar to those used in the first ocean steamers — are in working order, though today they are turned by an electric motor. The visitor can also see her stoke hold and boilers, the crew's quarters with an authentic lived-in appearance, the master's cabin and the drafty open wheelhouse.

The *Reliant* is part of a larger display explaining the development of the steamship, which includes another full-size vessel. This is the dainty steam launch *Donola* of 1893. Beneath and around the *Reliant* and the *Donola* are other full-size examples of marine steam, diesel and petrol engines, the rebuilt cabin of a Thames sailing barge and a liner's first-class cabin of the 1960s. These displays contrast in their different ways with accommodation on the *Reliant*. Around the walls of the hall there is a large display on port services such as lighthouses and light-ships, buoys, radar, pilots, tugs and dredgers, and also the museum's collection of wooden boats, both work boats and pleasure boats. They include a small fen lighter, a Norwegian rowing boat of obvious Viking descent, a novel North American boat with a wheel forward and handles aft so that it can be brought ashore in wheelbarrow fashion, the Dye's famous

Wayfarer dinghy used for some hair-raising long-distance voyages, and Prince Frederick's elegant eighteenth-century barge. There is also an authentically cluttered display of the interior of a boatbuilding shed. The best of the museum's collection of figureheads is also on display in the New Neptune Hall. There is more than enough to see in just this one area of the museum to fill a whole day's visit.

KENSINGTON
Science Museum, Exhibition Road, SW7 (telephone: 01-589 6371)
Open weekdays 10 — 6, Sunday 2 — 6.

An impressive maritime collection is an essential part of this large museum, whose brief is to cover the history and development of science and technology. The first displays were opened in 1857 at the South Kensington Museum, as a result of the Great Exhibition of 1851. In 1909 it became the Science Museum when the decorative art collections were separated to become the Victoria and Albert Museum.

The first group of displays is concerned with the development of the deep-sea sailing ship from ancient times to the late nineteenth-century four-masted barques. It includes models of many famous ships such as Columbus's *Santa Maria* and HMS *Victory*. A diorama of an Admiralty Board meeting of 1677 shows King Charles II and the members of the board debating the merits of a model for a new warship lying on the table before them. In a nearby case actual Navy Board models of the late seventeenth and eighteenth centuries are displayed. The superb miniature carvings decorating the bows, gunports and sterns of these models make them masterpieces of the ship modeller's art.

Another section is devoted to small craft. There are numerous examples of British regional boat types, all displayed against appropriate backgrounds. The quality of the models varies, but among the best are the model of the North Isles yole from the Shetlands and the contemporary model of an early nineteenth-century Yorkshire lugger. There are also many models from other parts of the world, including Chinese junks, African dugouts and North American birch-bark canoes.

There is an extensive display on the development of steamships, both merchant vessels and warships. They range from pioneer paddle steamers such as the *Savannah* (1819), the *Sirius* (1837) and the *Britannia* (the first Cunard liner, 1840) to the splendid builders' model of the four-funnel Union Castle liner *Arundel Castle* of 1921.

Propulsion is also covered in a separate section on marine engines. In this section there is a noteworthy collection of models of the different types of marine engine designed by Joseph Maudslay, one of the fathers of steam navigation, together with the original engine of the paddle steamer *Comet* of 1812 and one of the steam turbines from Parson's *Turbinia*. Within the same area, a bewildering array of nineteenth-century patent propeller designs is displayed. There is also another display on the evolution of marine boilers. Navigation, docks and harbours and diving are also covered in this most comprehensive of maritime exhibitions. Space permits only the mention of a few personal highlights for there is something in these displays to delight anyone remotely interested in the sea and ships.

SOUTHWARK
HMS Belfast, Symons Wharf, Vine Lane, Tooley Street, SE1. (telephone: 01-407 6434)

(Access also from the opposite bank by a ferry from the Tower of London landing stage.) Open daily (except Christmas Eve and Christmas Day) 11 — 6 (summer), 11 — 4.30 (winter).

HMS *Belfast* is the last of the Royal Navy's big-gun cruisers. She was designed for great speed, a long cruising range and the ability to protect convoys of merchant ships and take part in battles against large enemy warships. Her keel was laid in 1936 at Harland and Wolff's shipyard, Belfast, and she was launched fifteen months later but not handed over until August 1939. She measured 579 feet (176.5m) (between perpendiculars), with a breadth of 66 feet (20.1m) and a displacement of 11,550 tons (11,734.8t). She was equipped with four propellers driven by steam turbines, and she was capable of almost 33 knots (61km/hour). The main armour protecting her machinery and magazines was 4½ inches (114mm) thick, while her gun turrets and decks were strengthened by armour plate between 2 and 2½ inches (51-63mm) thick. She had a main armament of 12-inch (305mm) guns and a secondary armament of 4-inch (102mm) guns together with close-range anti-aircraft guns and torpedo tubes. Three amphibious Walrus spotter planes were carried. This formidable vessel carried a total complement of about 850 officers and men — almost the same number as Nelson's HMS *Victory*. She performed useful service on the northern patrol intercepting German merchant ships at the beginning of the Second World War. On 21st November 1939, after escorting a North Sea convoy, the *Belfast* was returning to Rosyth when she triggered a magnetic mine. The explosion severely damaged her hull and she spent the next three years in dock. In 1943 she was back in action guarding the vital convoys to Russia. In December 1943 she played an important part in the sinking of the German pocket battleship *Scharnhorst*. Later in the war she was part of the naval force which bombarded enemy positions during the invasion of Normandy in 1944, and the following year she was sent to the Far East.

After the Second World War she had one further period of active service during the Korean War. In the 1950s she was modernised and continued to serve in the Royal Navy until 1965. She subsequently became an accommodation and headquarters vessel at Portsmouth. The successful campaign to preserve her began as long ago as 1967. The Government eventually handed her over to the HMS *Belfast* Trust and a public appeal raised enough money for her conversion to a museum ship, the cost of towage to the Thames and her new berth opposite the Tower of London. All the important parts of the ship are open to the public including the bridge and fire director tower, the gun turrets and magazines, engine and boiler rooms, crew's quarters, the hospital, the fire control centre and workshops. They offer the visitor an insight into the complexities of a twentieth-century warship. There are also displays on the history of the ship and the development of cruisers.

Imperial War Museum, Lambeth Road, SE1 (telephone: 01-735 8922)
Open Monday to Saturday 10 — 6, Sunday 2 — 6 (except Good Friday, Christmas holidays and New Year's Day).

Built in 1815, the museum was formerly the Royal Hospital for the Insane, or 'Bedlam'. The museum was set up in 1920 to illustrate all aspects of the military operations of the First World War and has subsequently extended its collections to cover the Second World War and later operations. Its extensive displays include items of naval weaponry, uniforms, ship models and paintings. It also possesses a very large collection of photographs and documents.

TOWER HAMLETS
St Katharine's Yacht Haven, St Katharine's Way, E1
This ambitious project has been developed from the old St Katharine's dock, which was first opened in 1828. Originally most of the water space was surrounded by tall warehouses so that valuable cargoes could be directly unloaded from the ships into secure storage. Unfortunately most of the atmosphere of the original dock has been lost because in their efforts to make the scheme financially worthwhile the developers have pulled down all but two blocks of warehouses and erected an enormous concrete hotel, which dominates its surroundings. However, they have provided a very useful yacht harbour close to the City, and it has become a tourist attraction in its own right because of the number of historic vessels moored there. The most striking are the Thames barges with their red sails; during the winter months when there are no charters or racing as many as a dozen can be seen. The haven also contains some more permanent residents and these

include the lightship *Nore* and the steam tug *Challenge*, which dates from 1931. From 1st April to 30th September they are both open to the public daily (except Tuesdays and Wednesdays) from 10 till 5. The little double-ended steamer *Yarmouth* of 1895, which once carried summer trippers on the river Yare and the Broads, has been hoisted out of the water and now stands rather incongruously amid newly planted trees alongside a warehouse converted to an old-world pub. The privately owned Second World War 'puffer' *Vic 32* was also moored in the haven at the time of writing, and an old rowing lifeboat from the north-east coast, complete with her launching carriage, is displayed on the quayside. Her diagonal planking is very badly damaged and it is hoped that she will be restored.

It is likely that the Maritime Trust will move some of its ships to St Katharine's dock in the near future, including the *Kathleen and May*, the *Cambria*, the *Robin* and the *Lydia Eva* (see pages 19, 56 and 60).

WESTMINSTER
HMS Discovery, Victoria Embankment, WC2.
Open daily 1 — 4.15.

The *Discovery* was built in 1901 as an exploration vessel. She was commanded by Captain R. F. Scott on his expeditions to the Antarctic, including his last in 1904 when he and three companions died whilst returning from the South Pole. She was used on several later Antarctic surveys and her design was based on the stoutly built whaling ships that used to sail from Hull, Dundee and Peterhead. She is barque-rigged and carried quite a large sail area, which helped to eke out her coal supply on the long voyage to the Antarctic. Her wooden hull is constructed of the hardest wood to withstand the pressure of the ice.

The Victoria Embankment is also the mooring place of five other historic ships. The *Wellington* is a former naval sloop built in 1935 and now the headquarters of the Honourable Company of Master Mariners, and close to her lie the *President* and the *Chrysanthemum*, both First World War naval vessels converted as drill ships for the London division of the Royal Naval Reserve.

Further downstream lies the paddle steamer *Old Caledonia*. She was built by Denny of Dumbarton in 1934 as an excursion steamer for the Caledonia Steam Packet Company for service on the Clyde. On war service she served as a minesweeper and anti-aircraft ship, and on one occasion she shot down a German bomber and damaged another. She continued her Clyde sailings until 1969 and she is now converted into a floating pub and restaurant. Many of her original fittings have been retained, including her engines and paddles. Facilities include a restaurant, a cafeteria catering for all the family, three bars, shops and a deck for viewing the river. She

29

is open from 11 a.m. to 11 p.m. except Christmas Day, Boxing Day and New Year's Day.

Close by, the Embankment Gallery is housed in another paddle steamer, the *Tattershall Castle*. She was built as a Humber ferryboat in 1934. She was laid up in 1972 until purchased and converted to her new role. Fortunately much of her old woodwork, staircases and fittings has been retained, including her engines. She is open daily, except Monday, from 10 to 6.

HAMPSHIRE

BEAULIEU
Maritime Museum, Buckler's Hard (telephone: Buckler's Hard 203)
Open daily Easter to May 10 — 6, June to September 10 — 9, October to Easter 10 — 4.30.

This museum was opened in 1963 by Admiral of the Fleet Earl Mountbatten. It was once the New Inn and dates back to the times when the Hard was a thriving shipbuilding hamlet. The industry was established here because of the proximity of good supplies of oak timber. Many ships were built here for the Royal Navy, including HMS *Beaulieu*, a 30-gun frigate launched by Henry Adams in 1791 at a cost to the Admiralty of £12,250. Her model is on show. Most of the exhibits are related to the history of Buckler's Hard and the river Beaulieu: maps, plans of ships, documents, ship models, prints and drawings of the ships in action and their commanders. Also on view are a number of relics of Admiral Lord Nelson, including his baby clothes, a ring which he gave to Lady Hamilton and a letter he wrote on board HMS *Agamemnon* requesting more supplies of rope and canvas. Sir Francis Chichester's single-handed voyages are also commemorated.

EMSWORTH
Echo II, an oyster dredger of unique design and built about 1903, has for many years lain rotting in the harbour. A pamphlet on the Emsworth oyster smacks is available from D. J. Rudkin, 37 Ellesmere Orchard, Westbourne, Emsworth.

GOSPORT
Armaments Museum, Priddys Hard
Admission by appointment only.

This former gunpowder magazine has been converted into a museum to house a large collection of naval weapons, from muzzle-loading cannon to torpedoes. Related ship models also appear in the displays, including a large model of a powder-carrying Thames barge. In the little loading dock in front of the museum are moored two former naval steam launches, no. 463, tender to the royal yacht of 1899, and HSL (S) 376 of 1944, both owned by the Maritime Trust.

Royal Navy Submarine Museum, HMS Dolphin (telephone: Portsmouth 22351, extension 41868)

Admission by appointment only with visits office, any day except Sunday.

The Submarine Museum tells the story of the 'silent service' with models, photographs, relics, weapons and equipment. There is one full-size submarine — X-24, a midget submarine from the Second World War.

PORTSMOUTH
HMS Foudroyant

Visits by arrangement with the Captain Superintendent. Visible at anchor from both Portsmouth and Gosport.

A sailing frigate of twenty-six guns, originally named *Trincomalee* and built at Bombay in 1817. Her teak-built hull accounts for her longevity. In 1897 she replaced an older and larger vessel called *Foudroyant,* which was wrecked at Blackpool, and she is now used as a training ship for young people.

HMS Gannet, Fareham Creek

Not open to the public.

Owned by the Maritime Trust, HMS *Gannet* was built in 1878 as a naval sloop and is typical of the 'gunboats' that kept the peace in the distant parts of the British Empire. She is composite-built with wooden planking on an iron frame. To extend her range she was rigged as a three-masted ship and her propeller could be hoisted out of the water so that she could cruise under sail alone. For many years she was the training ship *Mercury* and at present she still has a Noah's ark roof which protects her hull and decks from the weather. The Maritime Trust plans to restore her full rig.

HMS Victory and Royal Naval Museum, HM Naval Base (telephone: Portsmouth 22351 extension 23868)

Open weekdays 10.30 — 5.30, Sunday 1 — 5.

HMS *Victory,* Lord Nelson's flagship at the battle of Trafalgar, now rests in a permanent berth at Portsmouth dockyard. She is both a memorial to Britain's most famous naval commander and a superb example of the sailing fighting ship. Her keel was laid in 1759 but she was not launched until 1765 and did not sail on her first commission until 1778. Her principal dimensions are: length on the waterline 152 feet 6 inches (46.5m), extreme beam 51 feet 10 inches (15.8m), depth of hold 21 feet 6 inches (6.4m), tonnage 2162 tons (2196.6t). 850 officers and men lived, worked and fought within the confined spaces of her hull. Her armament in Nelson's time consisted of twelve 12-pounder cannon on the quarter-deck, two 12-pounders and two 68-pounders on the forecastle, thirty 12-pounders on the upper deck, twenty-eight 24-pounders on the middle deck and thirty 32-pounders on the lower deck. She was also noted for her sailing qualities and several famous admirals used her as their flagship, including Kempenfelt, Howe, Hood and Lord St Vincent. She saw service in the American War of Independence and the war against revolutionary France, but by 1795 she was relegated to harbour service and then taken in for a major rebuilding, which lasted until 1803. Lord Nelson took her over as his flagship and she sailed in the fleet that blockaded Toulon and chased Villeneuve's French fleet across the Atlantic and back. This campaign led to the battle with the combined French and Spanish fleets off Cape Trafalgar on 21st October 1805. Her gallant admiral was killed during the course of the battle but the final outcome ensured British naval superiority for the rest of the war. After the battle she was badly damaged and spent two years refitting before being recommissioned. She was retained long after she had lost all battle capability as the flagship at Portsmouth. On a number of occasions she was threatened with scrapping and at least twice the monarch of the time intervened to save her. For over a century she remained afloat — a testimony to the enduring quality of English oak and the fine workmanship of her builders. In 1922 a public appeal was launched to restore her and purchase her a permanent dry berth. This was successful and since 1928 she has been on display to the general public. Visitors can roam the decks, which still carry a full armament of muzzle-loading guns together with all the crew's equipment.

The work of restoration is a continuing process: her oak timbers continue to decay and there is no more than about twenty per cent of original wood left in her. Much of the new wood is teak instead of oak. Her huge masts, which were originally built up of large pieces of pine, have been replaced by steel ones which pass through her keel to the dock floor in order not to strain her wooden framework, and much of the rigging, which is authentic, is now made of modern fibres such as terylene in place of the now scarce natural fibre hemp, which was the traditional material for ropes. Some areas of the ship may be closed to the public because of repair work.

As part of the restoration scheme for HMS *Victory* a naval museum was opened in 1930. The present building dates from 1938 and houses hundreds of exhibits relating to Lord Nelson and his career, including relics and furniture of HMS *Victory,* relics and models of other famous ships, naval uniforms, figureheads and navigational instruments. Many of Nelson's personal effects are on show together with paintings, prints, silverware, medallions

1. Coracles, once in common use in Wales and on the Severn, are of ancient design and are displayed in several museums, including the Welsh Folk Museum and Merseyside County Museums.

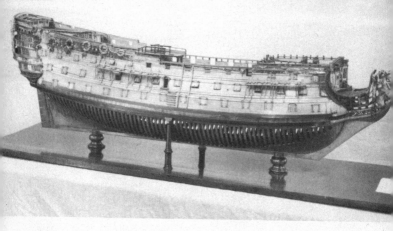

2. Navy Board models are noted for their splendid miniature carvings.
This is believed to be a model of the hundred-gun HMS St George
of 1714.

3. Half-models in their earliest form were used to design the lines
of the real ship. This model of the Two Sisters, a collier barque of
1783, is one such example.

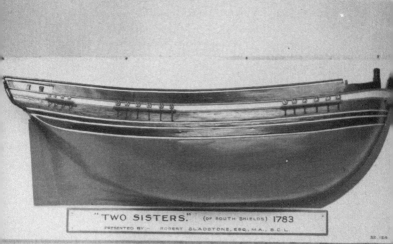

"TWO SISTERS." (OF SOUTH SHIELDS) 1783
PRESENTED BY - ROBERT GLADSTONE, ESQ., M.A., B.C.L.

4. Builders' models constructed at the same time as the full-size vessel exhibit a high degree of detail, as does this model of the steam yacht Banshee of 1900. It is a convention that the fittings are chrome- or silver-plated or in polished brass and not painted realistically.

5. Constructional models have one side unplanked to show their interior. This is a model of the Morecambe shrimping nobby Falcon. Many nobbies are still working or converted into sailing yachts.

6. French prisoner-of-war models contain the most incredibly delicate detail. This model is only 3⅝ inches (90mm) long.

7. SS Great Britain, Brunel's revolutionary vessel, in her most successful role as as Australian passenger ship. She is now preserved at Bristol.

8. Some of the floating exhibits at the Exeter Maritime Museum. In the background is the museum's largest craft, the Danish steam tug St Canute.

9. The Maritime Trust's Brixham trawler, Provident, with their
Bristol Channel pilot cutter, Kindly Light, alongside and their
schooner, Kathleen and May, in the background at Plymouth. The
Kindly Light is now displayed at Cardiff, while the Provident sails
in the Island Cruising Club fleet, Salcombe.

10. Barnabas, a Cornish lugger built in 1881 and restored to sailing condition by the Maritime Trust. She is moored at Penryn.

11. This state barge is part of the magnificent collection at the National Maritime Museum, Greenwich.

12. The tea clipper Cutty Sark, built at Dumbarton in 1869, is permanently preserved in a dry berth at Greenwich.

13. Gipsy Moth IV, displayed near the Cutty Sark at Greenwich, is the ketch in which Sir Francis Chichester sailed alone round the world in 1966.

14. The lightship Nore is one of the historic vessels preserved at St Katharine's Yacht Haven, near Tower Bridge in London.

15. The Maritime Trust's steam coaster, Robin, in her original condition at Coleraine in 1898. She is undergoing restoration at Rochester.

16. The Maritime Trust's Thames sailing barge, Cambria, berthed at Rochester. She was the last British-registered vessel to trade under sail alone.

17. HMS Victory is preserved in a dry berth at Portsmouth Dockyard. Launched in 1765, she was Nelson's flagship, aboard which he was killed, at Trafalgar in 1805.

18. A model of Hull sailing trawler H1240 is the centrepiece of a display at the Town Docks Museum, Hull.

19. The Humber keel Comrade has been restored to sailing condition, except for her leeboards, by the Humber Keel and Sloop Preservation Society, and is based at Beverley.

20. Turbinia, the first turbine-powered ship, was built by Charles Parsons in 1894. She is now preserved at the Science Museum, Newcastle.

21. The last sea-going paddle steamer in the world, the Waverley, is a popular attraction for tourists, giving cruises on the Clyde.

22. *The topsail schooner Result undergoing restoration at Harland and Wolff's yard in Belfast. She is to be displayed at the Ulster Folk and Transport Museum, Holywood.*

23. A model of the Leith 'baldie' Refuge, 1883, at the Scottish Fisheries Museum, Anstruther, Fife.

and the great man's death mask. In the centre of the main hall is the state barge used to convey Nelson's coffin from Greenwich to Whitehall stairs on 8th January 1806. An annexe at the back of the museum houses the magnificent panoramic painting by W. L. Wyllie of the battle of Trafalgar. As funds permit, it is hoped to extend the displays in the adjacent late eighteenth-century store buildings. The first phase of this extension has been opened. It houses a collection of prints, paintings, ceramics, miniatures and medallions, all commemorating Nelson and his times, presented to the Royal Navy by Mrs J. G. MacCarthy, OBE.

Royal Marines Museum, Eastway Barracks (telephone: Portsmouth 22351 extension 6132-6135)
Open Monday to Friday 10 — 4, Saturday and Sunday 10 — 12.
The museum enjoys the splendid setting of the former Royal Marines officers' mess and tells the story of the sea-going soldiers from 1664 to the present day. Displays include a model of HMS *Mars*, an eighteenth-century two-decker, and HMS *Albion*, a modern commando carrier. Eighteenth-century lower-deck life is reconstructed in another display, and there are also good prints of eighteenth- and nineteenth-century sea battles in which the Royal Marines played a vital role.

Southsea Castle, Clarence Esplanade (telephone: Portsmouth 24584)
Open September to April 10.30 — 5.30, May to August 10.30 — 9.
The castle, which was built by Henry VIII in 1538-45 as part of a chain of coastal defences, contains displays of local military history, including one of outstanding maritime interest on the *Mary Rose*. This warship was built for Henry VIII in 1509 and rebuilt in 1536. She was a key vessel in the history of naval warfare, having been built in the transitional period between fortified ships manned by soldiers and the later heavy-gunned vessels crewed by seamen.

In July 1545 France and England were at war, and the French sent a fleet of over two hundred ships to attack England's naval base at Portsmouth. King Henry was present at Southsea Castle when the French were sighted. He ordered his fleet to attack, but the weather was so calm that several French rowing galleys were able to fire on the English ships with impunity. Then a favourable wind sprang up and in their turn the English fleet got under way. The 700-ton (711t) *Mary Rose*, one of the king's principal ships, was commanded by Vice-Admiral Sir George Carew. As she was manoeuvring for the attack, she heeled over so that the sills of her lower gunports, normally only 16 inches (406mm) above the waterline, went under. Her heavy guns broke away from their lashings, making her even more unstable. There was complete panic aboard and within minutes she filled with water and sank, with the loss of all four hundred of her crew. Meanwhile the French were beaten off, abandoning their treasure ship in their retreat. Shortly after her sinking unsuccessful attempts were made to salvage the *Mary Rose*. Three hundred years later, in 1840, during salvage work on the neighbouring wreck of the *Royal George*, some of her guns were raised. She was rediscovered in 1969 and is now the subject of a systematic archaeological excavation. Some of the finds are displayed at Southsea Castle, including examples of her iron guns.

SOUTHAMPTON
HMS Cavalier, moored off Mayflower Park
Not yet open to the public

The last of the distinguished C class of Second World War destroyers completed in 1944 by Whites at Cowes, HMS *Cavalier* is now to be restored by a specially established trust.

Maritime Museum, Wool House, Bugle Street (telephone: Southampton 23941)
Open weekdays 11 — 1, 2 — 5; Sundays 2 — 5.

The Wool House, as the name suggests, was built as a wool warehouse in the fourteenth century. At that time Southampton was the principal port for the export of West Country wool to European weavers of fine woollens. Later, in the sixteenth century, it was used to store alum, and in the eighteenth century it housed French and Spanish prisoners of war.

One of the main exhibits is the fine model of HMS *Temeraire* made by French prisoners of war. Photographic panels illustrate the development of the port, and there are models of types of vessel calling at Southampton from ocean liners to paddle ferries.

HEREFORD AND WORCESTER
WORCESTER
Spry (Severn trow), Diglis Basin

Severn trows were the sailing barges of the Severn. Their name is said to derive from the Anglo-Saxon word for a drinking vessel or trough. They came in at least two distinct varieties: the up-river version with clinker hull and squaresail, a replica of which is to be built for the Ironbridge Gorge Museum, and the lower river or estuary type with carvel hull, transom stern, open hold and sloop or ketch rig. The *Spry*, one of the latter type, is now used as a workshop. She is probably the last of her type in anything approaching sound condition. Another trow, the *Hannah*, may still be afloat as a houseboat, and there are also a number of beached hulks on Lydney marshes. The Severn Trow Preservation Society has just been set up to restore the *Spry*.

HUMBERSIDE

BRIDLINGTON
Bridlington Art Gallery and Museum, Sewerby Hall (telephone: Bridlington 77874)
Open Easter to September, Sunday to Friday 10 — 12.30, 1.30 — 6; Saturday 1.30 — 6.

A small display of ship models is one of the many collections housed in this seventeenth-century house.

GOOLE
The Library and Museum
Open weekdays during library hours.

The museum is above the library and deals mainly with the history of the port, which was founded in the early nineteenth century as a transhipment point between sea-going and inland waterway traffic. The work of Reuben Chappell, the local marine artist who specialised in watercolour portraits of coastal sailing craft, is well represented, and there are also builder's half-models of locally owned steamers. Some of the sailing-ship models are rather rough.

GRIMSBY
Doughty Museum, Town Hall Square (telephone: Grimsby 59161)
Open Tuesday to Saturday 10 — 12.30, 2 — 5.30.

A fine and varied collection of ship models. It is appropriate that this fishing port should possess a good collection of models of fishing boats. There are different types of sailing fishing craft including a Barking smack, luggers from Mount's Bay and Hastings, a Yarmouth herring drifter and Brixham trawler, and a comprehensive collection of builders' models of local steam trawlers, some of which, like the *Chilian* of 1883, date back to the first years of power trawling. Some of the remaining exhibits, while having little relevance to the area, are of superb quality: for example, the contemporary rigged sailing warships the frigate *Caledonia* and the French battleships *Le Triomphant* of 1778 and *L'Ocean* of 1785.

KINGSTON UPON HULL
Humber Keel and Sloop Preservation Society Ltd
Secretary Mr C. C. Lodge, Glenlea, New Ellerby, near Hull.

This enterprising group owns the Humber keel *Comrade,* which is now almost restored, and the sloop *Amy Howson.* The *Comrade* is normally based at Beverley Beck, Beverley, on the river Hull. She is a steel-hulled vessel built in 1923, on the traditional bluff lines of the Humber keel, and rigged with a square mainsail and topsail. During the summer she makes a number of trips under sail, details of which are announced in the society's newsletter.

51

There are also open days for the general public. Most of the restoration work, including that on the rigging, has been carried out by members of the society. The *Amy Howson*, the sloop, was gaff-rigged. She was built at Beverley in 1914 and was acquired by the society after the *Comrade*. So far work has been concentrated on putting her steel hull back into sound condition. At present she lies at South Ferriby sluice on the south bank of the Humber and she too is open to the public on the society's open days.

The keel was essentially a cargo vessel for inland water transport and was formerly common on the Humber and all its tributaries. It was also the sole surviving type of large craft fitted with a single square-rigged mast. They appear to be of ancient origin, for much of their rigging, especially the pear-shaped deadeyes for tightening the shrouds, resembles that of Elizabethan craft. They were very bluff in the bows to maximise their cargo capacity, while the stern was more rounded to assist the vessel to respond more readily to the helm, an essential quality on the many miles of narrow waterway. They had a reputation for being able to sail very close to the wind and they were fitted with leeboards to help them when going to windward. Before the introduction of iron and steel hulls they were built in oak, either in carvel or clinker form or in a combination of the two. A number of keels traded under sail into the 1930s and many more were motorised or turned into dumb barges. The sloop has a similar hull form to the keel, but was rigged with a gaff mainsail and jib. A number of keels and sloops survive in various states of repair, including the restored wooden keel *Annie Maud* at York, the 'west country keel' *Ethel* at the Canal Boat Museum, Ellesmere Port, and the *Mayday* at Goole, the decaying relic of an earlier preservation attempt.

Paddle steamer Lincoln Castle, Corporation Pier, Hull, or New Holland Pier

The last coal-fired paddle ferry in commission on the Humber, the *Lincoln Castle* was built in 1940 by A. & J. Inglis on the Clyde. She will continue to run across the Humber until the completion of the new Humber Bridge. She also sails on river excursions during the summer, and there is a campaign to preserve her in working condition after the end of the ferry service. Unfortunately this will be a very expensive project.

Town Docks Museum, Queen Victoria Square (telephone: Hull 27625 or 224316)

Open weekdays 10 — 5.30, Sunday 2.30 — 4.30.

This maritime museum is a replacement of the old Hull Maritime Museum at Pickering Park. It is housed in the grand former office building of the Hull Docks Authority. The preparation of displays is still in progress. So far, galleries about whaling and fishing have been opened to the public and late in 1978 a new display will be opened which will include the development of merchant shipping, navigation, the history of Hull docks and Hull shipowners, together with a display on local nautical archaeology with particular reference to the prehistoric vessels found at North Ferriby. A final phase to be opened in about 1980 will include marine engineering and modern navigational instruments. It is also hoped to provide a reference library and plan room for researchers.

The whaling industry of Hull flourished in the late eighteenth and early nineteenth centuries. Stoutly built sailing vessels of about 300 to 400 tons (300-400t) sailed to Arctic waters to catch whales for their blubber, to boil down for whale oil, and their baleen or 'whalebone' from the jaws, which, because of its strength and flexibility, had a great many uses before the invention of plastics. It was particularly useful in the construction of ladies' corsets! The whales were caught by the use of hand harpoons thrown from small open boats, of which each whaling ship carried six or seven. Early in the nineteenth century harpoon guns were developed but at first they were only of limited use because they could be fired only at point-blank range and took time to reload.

By the middle of the century Hull's whalers had lost ground to their rivals at Dundee and Peterhead, where steam-powered whalers had been successfully introduced, and the last Hull whaler, the *Diana* — a steam auxiliary — sailed on her last voyage in 1869. The whaling gallery has been cleverly designed to make the maximum use of the space available, with the displays in two levels. The main displays cover the natural history of the whale and its hunting and processing, with a fearful array of harpoons, flenching knives and other implements for ripping away the blubber. There is a reconstruction of the bows of a whaleboat complete with all its equipment, and a very fine selection of paintings of whaling scenes by local marine artists. The most notable are those by John Ward, who was probably the only whaling painter to visit the Arctic. There are also a number of models of whalers, mostly sailor-made, and many relics, including mementoes of the last sailing whaler, the *Truelove*, built in 1764 and still at work in the 1860s. A particular highlight of this Hull museum is the small gallery devoted to the collection of scrimshaw — the engraving of designs on whalebone, sperm-whale teeth or walrus tusks, the traditional art of whaling men.

As whaling died in the 1860s fishing grew, with the spread of railways for inland distribution of the catches and the later introduction of steam trawling. The fisheries display deals with the older methods of inshore fishing along the Yorkshire coast and trawling, both under sail and power. It includes full-size examples of fishing gear, for example a crab pot, a line 300 fathoms (548.6m) long and an eighteen-trawl door from a modern vessel. To explain how the fishing gear worked, there are models of the boats and their nets or lines set in perspex seas, both to the same scale. Only the depth of water, which would be impossibly deep for the showcases, is out of scale. The displays go into detail on the fishing grounds and the old practice of fishing in fleets with steam carriers to bring the fish to Billingsgate market. Another section covers the occasion on 21st and 22nd October 1964 when a Hull fishing fleet was fired on by Russian warships in mistake for Japanese torpedo boats, and this includes a most evocative relic — the splinter-torn companionway of the trawler *Mino*. Further sections deal with fish-finding techniques, a working model of a testing tank for trawl nets, the fishermen and the Royal National Mission to Deep Sea Fishermen.

These displays make this museum one of the best maritime museums in Britain.

SCUNTHORPE
Normanby Hall (telephone: Scunthorpe 720215)
Open April to October, weekdays except Tuesday 10 — 12.30, Sunday 2 — 5.30; November to March, Monday to Friday 10 — 12.30, 2 — 5, Sunday 2 — 5.

Normanby Hall is not worth a special excursion for the nautical enthusiast unless combined with a trip to Grimsby and South Ferriby to see the Humber sloop *Amy Howson*. The Regency house contains an excellent bone French prisoner-of-war model of a three-decker warship and several smaller examples of the same genre, which are stored in the upper shelves of one of the bookcases of the library. There are also some marine paintings — mainly of fishing boats — on the first-floor landing.

ISLE OF WIGHT
COWES
Cowes Maritime Museum, Cowes Library, Beckford Road (telephone: Cowes 3341)
Open Monday to Friday 9.30 — 6, Saturday 9 — 5.

In a gallery above the library is a display of relics of the local shipbuilding industry over the last century. It is possible that a separate maritime museum for the Isle of Wight might be established in the future.

Endeavour
One of the huge J Class yachts, the *Endeavour* was built in 1934 to sail against the American yacht *Rainbow* for that most elusive of yachting prizes, the America's Cup. She is now owned by the Maritime Trust and berthed at Souter's yard.

Medway Queen and Ryde Queen

These two paddle steamers at the Isle of Wight Marina were both saved from the breaker's yard for preservation and are both in a sorry state after a few years. The *Medway Queen* has been abandoned while the *Ryde Queen* has recently suffered a fire whilst serving as a 'boatel' and night club. They are an object lesson to all would-be ship preservationists of the terrible difficulties in keeping old vessels afloat and viable.

WHIPPINGHAM

Folly Inn is the headquarters of a flotilla of interesting 'old gaffers'. The inn itself was originally housed in the beached hull of a local wooden barge but it has been so extended and altered over the years that very little of the original vessel remains.

KENT

BORSTAL
Paddle steamer Kingswear Castle, Medway Marina

A small excursion steamer built in 1924 at Dartmouth for excursions on the river Dart and now being restored by the Paddle Steamer Preservation Society.

CHATHAM
HM Dockyard
Not open to the public.

Several remarkable eighteenth- and early nineteenth-century shipbuilding sheds and workshops and a good collection of figureheads.

International Towing Limited and Medway Maritime Museum

This enterprising new company has been set up to operate steam tugs for commercial towage. At the time of writing the fleet consists of the *Cervia*, a wartime design built at Aberdeen in 1946, and the *Goliath*, a former Admiralty deep-sea towage and salvage tug. In conjunction with the Medway Maritime Museum, the company also supports the TID tug *Hercules*, dating from the Second World War, and the former Tees paddle tug *John H. Amos*, which has been renamed *Hero*. No details of siting or public admission were available at the time of writing.

DEAL
Maritime Museum, 22 St Georges Road
Open Spring Bank Holiday to end of September, daily 2 — 5.

The beach boats of Deal were once of considerable importance because of their work among the fleets of sailing ships which often anchored in the Downs waiting for favourable winds to enable them to proceed down the Channel or up to the Thames estuary. These beach boats ferried pilots, passengers and stores out to the anchored vessels. They were stoutly constructed, clinker-built open boats which had to stand the strain of frequent launchings from the steeply shelving shingle beach. They were built in several different sizes for different functions. The luggers were designed for transporting stores and were capable of carrying anchors and cable for ships in distress, while the pilot galleys were designed for taking pilots off ships in the Downs. They were rigged with a large dipping lugsail and could be rowed as well. When under sail they attained a considerable speed. The museum has preserved three types of Deal boat: a small 14-foot (4.3m) punt; the *Secret,* a punt rigged with main and mizzen lugsails; and the galley *Saxon King.* There are also other relics from the sailing-ship days of this famous anchorage.

DOVER

Dover Museum, Ladywell (telephone: Dover 201066)
Open weekdays (except Wednesday), winter 10 — 12, 2 — 4.30, summer 10 — 1, 2 — 6.

Local history displays include ship models and the history of the medieval Cinque Ports.

ROCHESTER

Cambria (sailing barge), The Esplanade (telephone: 01-730 0096)
Open Easter to September, daily 11 — 6.

An excellent example of a coastal-going Thames barge, known as a 'mulie' barge because of her gaff-rigged mizzen in place of the normal small spritsail. She was built in 1906 and continued carrying cargoes up the east coast to such ports as Great Yarmouth and Norwich until 1971 when she was the last vessel on the British register carrying cargo under sail alone. She is now preserved by the Maritime Trust, which has set up an exhibition and bookstall in her hold. She may move to St Katharine's Dock, London, in the near future.

Robin (steam coaster), Doust's Yard
Not open to the public.

The *Robin,* which was built in 1890, is probably the last example of the once familiar 'dirty British coaster', of Masefield's famous poem. She has the usual arrangement of engines aft and bridge amidships. She was still trading under the Spanish flag until she was purchased by the Maritime Trust in 1974. Restoration work has so far concentrated on making her existing structure sound, although some progress has been made towards restoring her to her appearance of 1890. The *Robin* also is likely to move to St Katharine's Dock, London.

Rochester Public Museum, Eastgate House (telephone: Medway 44176)
Open daily (except Friday) 2 — 5.30.
   Ship models in the collections include good models of a spritsail barge and a fishing bawley and French prisoner-of-war models produced at Rochester Castle.

LANCASHIRE

FLEETWOOD
Fleetwood Maritime Museum, Fleetwood Library, Dock Street (telephone: Preston 54868 extension 6274)
Open during library hours.
   A small exhibition depicting the history of this nineteenth-century port, which was developed as a cross-channel port and commercial rival to Liverpool, and which eventually found prosperity as a fishing port. Displays include interesting photographs of fishing craft and a small collection of marine paintings of local cross-channel steamers.

LANCASTER
Lancaster Museum, Old Town Hall, Market Square (telephone: Lancaster 64637)
Open weekdays 10 — 5.
   Lancaster was a major port in the eighteenth century, but its development was hampered by the silting of the river Lune. The quayside, with its splendid customs house and eighteenth-century warehouses, is well worth a visit, as is Glasson Dock, an early nineteenth-century enclosed dock connected with the Lancaster Canal at the mouth of the Lune. The museum has plans for a maritime museum and is also active in trying to save an early dry-dock at Glasson Dock. The displays in the Old Town Hall include quite a number of objects of maritime interest such as the excellent contemporary model of the local privateer *Thetis* and the half-models of the iron sailing ships built by the short-lived Lancaster Iron Shipbuilding Co in the late 1860s. The steam dredger *Mannin* also still works on the Lune.

MERSEYSIDE

BIRKENHEAD
Wirral Museum, Williamson Art Gallery, Slatey Road (telephone: 051-652 4177)
Open weekdays 10 — 5 (Thursday 10 — 9), Sunday 2 — 5.
   There are two galleries of maritime interest. One contains a display of builders' models, mainly of ships built at the Birkenhead shipyard of Cammell-Laird & Company. These include a model of the second *Mauretania,* launched at Birkenhead in 1939. The second gallery has a good display of models of

Birkenhead ferryboats, marine paintings and relics of the *Lottie Sleigh* explosion. There is also a poor model of the famous Confederate commerce-raider *Alabama*, which was built in Birkenhead.

The same local authority also has a number of other marine paintings and models of Wallasey ferryboats at the Library, Earlston Road, Wallasey.

LIVERPOOL
Merseyside County Museums, William Brown Street (telephone: 051-207 0001)
Open weekdays 10 — 5, Sunday 2 — 5 (except Christmas, Boxing Day and Good Friday).

This museum has a major collection of ship models, pictures and relics which it hopes to display in a waterfront maritime museum. Meanwhile the present museum houses a representative selection of the finest objects in the collections. There are three main areas of maritime interest: the Port of Liverpool Gallery, which is concerned with the social and maritime history of the city; the History of the Ship Gallery, which traces the development of boats and ships from prehistoric times to the present day; and the Natural History Gallery, which includes sections on whaling and fishing.

On entering the Port of Liverpool Gallery, which leads directly off the main entrance, one is confronted by the huge figurehead from HMS *Hastings*, a sailing warship of 1818 that acted as the guardship for Liverpool for many years. To the right of the great panorama of the river Mersey in 1866 there is a series of displays which illustrates the development of the port and its commerce from the eighteenth century to the present day, including such themes as the slave trade, the development of marine steam engines, emigration and the two world wars. There are also sections on port services such as dredging, pilotage, tidal predictions, lifesaving and docks, with displays on the coastal trade, shipbuilding and the social history of the seafarer. The exhibition is dominated by a very large display case which houses models of locally owned ships from 1851 to 1948, all built to the same scale (1:48) and to the same waterline. These include the famous clipper *Flying Cloud*, nineteenth-century passenger liners — the *City of Paris* (1866), the *Gallia* (1879) and the *Vancouver* of 1884 — tugs, a tanker, cargo liners, and a spectacular 20-foot-long (6.1m) model of the Cunard Line's *Berengaria* (formerly *Imperator*).

The History of the Ship Gallery contains a full-size coracle from the river Dee, a model boat from an ancient Egyptian tomb, some very detailed models of different types of marine steam engine, and many other models and illustrations. The museum also holds special temporary exhibitions on maritime subjects.

Ship models can be seen in many other local institutions, for example in the main hall of the Mersey Dock & Harbour Company's offices at the Pier Head. The company also owns a number of interesting steam vessels, including the giant floating crane *Mammoth*, built in 1914, and the busy tenders *Vigilant* and *Salvor*.

Sudley Art Gallery, Mossley Hill Road.
Open weekdays 10 — 5, Sunday 2 — 5.
The former home of a member of a prominent local shipowning family. One room contains a display of ship models from the County Museum's collection.

SOUTHPORT
Botanic Gardens Museum, Churchtown (telephone: Southport 27547)
Open weekdays 10 — 5 (summer 10 — 6), Sunday 2 — 5 (dusk in winter).
A local and natural history museum with a well-preserved example of a dugout canoe and displays on the local shrimping industry, lifeboats and a builders' half-model of the steam coaster *White Rose*.

NORFOLK

Albion (wherry)
The *Albion* is the last Norfolk trading wherry afloat and under sail. Wherries were the cargo carriers of the Norfolk Broads and the connecting network of rivers, and by the 1930s only a few were left sailing. In 1949 the Norfolk Wherry Trust was established to keep one of them sailing. The *Albion*, built in 1898, was selected and the Trust has succeeded in keeping her sailing ever since. Initially she carried cargo but as cargoes became difficult to obtain she has been chartered for summer cruising. The wherry's rig consists of a stout mast, mounted in a forward position and capable of being lowered for 'shooting' bridges, and a black high-peaked gaffsail without a boom. Wherries could sail extremely close to the wind. The *Albion* is not a typical wherry because she is carvel and not clinker built. Some other wherries have been converted to houseboats, including the *Bramble* and the *Hathor* at Martham, while the *Olive* pleasure wherry — a purpose-built Broads yacht with wherry rig — has recently been restored to sailing condition. Norfolk County Museums Service also has care of the wherry *Lord Roberts*, which is sunk near Horning, and it is hoped to restore her as soon as possible. The *Albion* is normally cruising in spring and summer and at other times is usually moored at Horning Rectory or on Oulton Broad Dyke. Details from the Hon. Secretary, Norfolk Wherry Trust, The Croft, Norwich Road, Lingwood, Norfolk.

BRUNDALL

SS *Resolute,* a small excursion steamer which ran on trips between Great Yarmouth and Gorleston and on the Broads from 1903 until 1968, is now being restored to steaming condition by the Veteran Steamship Society.

GREAT YARMOUTH

Lydia Eva (steam drifter), South Quay (near Town Hall) (telephone: Great Yarmouth 55746, or 01-730 0096)
Open daily (except Saturday) June to September 10 — 1, 2 — 6

The famous Yarmouth herring fishery attracted hundreds of fishing boats in its heyday and the *Lydia Eva* is the last remaining steam drifter. She was built for Mr H. Eastick of Great Yarmouth. She was a successful boat but the depressed state of fishing in the 1930s forced her owner to sell her to the Air Ministry in 1938 for use as a buoy and mooring tender. For her new work she was considerably altered. In 1972 she was purchased and restored by the Maritime Trust. Her galley and crew's accommodation have been returned to their original appearance. Her engines and boiler have been maintained in working condition and she has made a sea trip round to King's Lynn where she was built. Her fish hold has been converted into an exhibition about her history and that of the Great Yarmouth herring industry, with fishing gear, photographs and models. She may move to St Katharine's Dock, London, in the near future.

Maritime Museum of East Anglia, Marine Parade (opposite the Bathing Pool) (telephone: Great Yarmouth 2267)
Open June to September daily, 10 — 1, 2 — 8; October to May, weekdays 10 — 1, 2 — 5.30.

This museum is housed in the historic shipwrecked sailors' home. The displays occupy three floors of the large Victorian building, with good views of Yarmouth Roads and passing coastal traders. The collections are centred on the history and activities of the port of Yarmouth and its hinterland, the Norfolk Broads. The principal displays on the ground floor are about the Yarmouth herring fisheries and the local shipbuilding industry. There is an excellent collection of models, including several contemporary models of early nineteenth-century sailing ships from fishing luggers to full-rigged ships.

Upstairs, the themes of the displays include lifesaving on the Norfolk coast, the North Sea oil industry and the Norfolk wherry. This is an outstanding collection of models, and it is accompanied by an equally outstanding collection of relics, photographs and pictures. There is a unique paper cut-out model of a shipyard at Wells on the north Norfolk coast and a museum within a museum of bizarre objects left by sailors staying at the home. Behind the main building a temporary shelter has been erected to house a number of full-size specimens, which can be viewed by arrangement. These include the old lateen-rigged Broads yacht *Maria*, a Blakeney mussel punt, a Rob Roy canoe, and a timber bob for hauling heavy logs to the shipyard.

KING'S LYNN
Lynn Museum (next to the bus station) (telephone: King's Lynn 5001)
Open Monday to Saturday 10 — 5.

The local history section contains objects connected with the history of this ancient port, including a picture model of an early nineteenth-century shipyard, the light from the first Lynn Well light-vessel and a board from the local pilot's office showing the names and signals of locally owned ships. The Fisher Fleet to the north of the town centre is still the base of Lynn's fishing boats, some of which are former sailing smacks.

NORWICH
Bridewell Museum of Local Industries, Bridewell Alley (telephone: Norwich 22233)
Open weekdays 10 — 5.

A medieval house, later used as the city bridewell (gaol). Among the extensive displays of local crafts and industries is one on boatbuilding on the Norfolk Broads. It includes a very good selection of builders' half-models of local yachts, boatbuilding tools, and possibly the best collection of wherry vanes anywhere. Wherries were the sailing barges of the Broads and each one carried a distinctive metal wind-vane at her masthead, with several yards of red bunting attached to it.

Lightship, Riverside Road.
Not open to the public.

A preserved lightship is moored on the river Yare close to the railway station. It serves as the headquarters of the local Sea Cadet Corps.

NORTHAMPTONSHIRE
STOKE BRUERNE
The Waterways Museum (telephone: Northampton 862229)
Open daily (summer) 10 — 6.

The museum is housed in a converted canal warehouse overlooking one of the locks of the Grand Union Canal, not far from the entrance of the famous Blisworth Tunnel. Exhibits have been gathered from all parts of the canal system; the most eye-catching is the reconstruction of the stern section of the narrowboat *Happy Valley*. This is complete with the boatman's cabin and all its traditional paintwork and decorations. Other displays include more examples of painted cans, dippers and utensils, boatmen's and women's traditional costumes, models of boats and canal features such as the Foxton inclined plane and the Anderton boat lift, together with a vast array of photographs, prints and relics. Outside, a full-size narrowboat is displayed in a boat-weighing machine. There are also excursions by narrowboat to the Blisworth Tunnel.

NORTHUMBERLAND
BAMBURGH
Grace Darling Museum
Open 1st April to mid October, daily 11 — 7.

The story of how Grace Darling and her father, the keeper of the Longstone lighthouse, rowed out to rescue the survivors of the wreck of the *Forfarshire* in 1838 is well known, and since her death in 1842 exhibits connected with her and her family have been gathered for display here. The chief exhibit is the coble used in the rescue. It is the type of boat used by fishermen of the north-east coast and was built for Grace Darling's father in 1828.

NORTH YORKSHIRE
SCARBOROUGH
Rotunda Museum, Vernon Road (telephone: Scarborough 67326)
Open weekdays 10 — 1, 2 — 5; Sunday (Spring Bank Holiday to 30th September) 2 — 5.

Upstairs, in what must be a unique circular 'double-decker' exhibition with a travelling viewing platform, there are sailor-made models and marine paintings, reminders of Scarborough's rich maritime past. There is a particularly good ship portrait of the brig *Imogene*. Some maritime exhibitions are also at the lighthouse at the harbour entrance. This is open daily during the summer. The most interesting objects are a pair of cased half-models which show two local sailing ships on the stocks ready for launching.

WHITBY
Whitby Lifeboat Museum, on the quay at the bottom of the Khyber Pass
Open daily throughout the summer.

The rather informal displays contain a wealth of photographs of past Whitby lifeboats and their rescues, with a large scale model of the wreck of the steamer *Rohilla* as a centrepiece. There are many sailor-made models, including a particularly good one of a sailing coble, and three builders' models of locally owned deep-sea steamers of Headlam & Company.

Whitby Museum, Pannet Park (telephone: Whitby 2908)
Open May to September 9 — 5.30, Sunday 2 — 5; October to
April weekdays 10.30 — 1 (Wednesday and Saturday also 2 — 4),
Sunday 2 — 4.

This museum of the Whitby Literary and Philosophical Society
contains a shipping gallery with a wide variety of models, including a large scale model of a brig, a very fine French prisoner-
of-war model in bone, local fishing boats and locally owned tramp
steamers. There is also a model of Captain Cook's ship,
Resolution, together with other relics of the famous explorer. In a
separate gallery on whaling there are displays on the two
Scoresbys, who also came from Whitby (see also Hull, Town Docks
Museum for further Scoresby material).

YORK
National Railway Museum, Leeman Road (telephone: York 21261)
Open Monday to Saturday 10 — 6, Sunday 2.30 — 6 (except
Christmas holidays, New Year's Day and Good Friday).

At first sight one would not associate this splendid museum,
containing over forty full-size locomotives and carriages, with
anything remotely nautical. But the railways, as operators of cross-
channel ferries, were and are major shipowners, and on the first
floor above the main hall there is a representative selection of
models of their ships. They include nineteenth-century paddle
steamers such as the *Rose* of 1876 and the *Beatrice* of 1882, which
belonged to the London & North Western Railway, the Great
Central Railway's steamer *Dewsbury* of 1910, and one of the first
specialised car ferries — the *Autocarrier* of 1931. Perhaps the
most intriguing model is that of the de-luxe cabin (complete with
bathroom) for the Heysham-Northern Ireland steamer *Duke of
Lancaster* of 1928.

York Castle Museum, Tower Street (telephone: York 53611)
Open April to September weekdays 9.30 — 6, Sunday 10 — 6;
October to March weekdays 9.30 — 4.30, Sunday 10 — 4.30.

A vast folk museum with period rooms and a replica of a
Victorian street, but with a few items of nautical interest. These
are housed in a small room off one of the first-floor exhibition
halls and include a Navy Board model of the 70-gun HMS *Berwick*
of 1718, a builders' model of the paddle steamer *Ashton*, and
several sailor-made models, including a most delightful picture
model containing a whole fleet of small sailing vessels.

The privately owned and restored Humber keel *Annie Maud* is
also worth a visit. At present she is moored close to the Lendal
Bridge at the quay in North Street. She is open to visitors in the
summer, with an exhibition in her hold.

SALOP

TELFORD
Ironbridge Gorge Museum, Ironbridge village and neighbouring area of the Severn Gorge (telephone: Ironbridge 3522)
Open daily 10 — 6.

This is one of the most exciting open-air museums in Britain. It is based on a unique series of industrial monuments of the eighteenth-century iron, coal-mining, brickmaking and pottery industries of the area. Water transport by the river Severn and the Shropshire Canal was of vital importance. At the Blist's Hill Open Air Museum the old Shropshire Canal has been re-excavated and the spectacular inclined plane which carried tub boats down and up from the river Severn has been partially reinstated. One of the iron tub boats was discovered on a local farm serving as a water tank. It has now been restored and floats in the canal, along with the Shropshire Union Canal icebreaker *Middlewich*. Plans are in hand for the building of a replica Severn barge or trow to be displayed at the information centre — a nineteenth-century Gothic warehouse — in Ironbridge village. These vessels were clinker-built, with a single square sail. Many of them were built in the eighteenth-century shipyards that flourished on the opposite bank of the Severn. Close to the Iron Bridge itself — the first in the world — lies the workshop of the last surviving maker of coracles on the river. These light portable boats of ancient design were in common use for fishing and ferrying until recent times.

SOMERSET

BRIDGWATER
Blake Museum, Blake Street (telephone: Bridgwater 2597)
Open daily 10 — 1, 2 — 5 (closes at 1 on Tuesday).

The great Admiral Blake was born in this house in 1599, according to local tradition. Displays include Blake relics, displays about the battle of Santa Cruz and other sea battles, and a shipping gallery with photographs of local vessels.

WATCHET
Market House Museum
To be opened in July 1978

This museum of local history places particular emphasis on the town's old yet still working harbour. Displays include several models and pictures by Captain Thomas Chidgey, a Watchet seafarer, a model of a tramway for carrying local iron ore from the mine to the quayside for shipment, the figurehead of a local ship and other items of ship's equipment, together with old photographs of the port and its shipping.

SOUTH YORKSHIRE

DONCASTER
Cusworth Hall, Cusworth Lane (telephone: Doncaster 61842)
Open weekdays 11 — 5, Sunday 2 — 5 (in winter closes at 4).

A folk museum with one gallery devoted to the canals and waterways of South Yorkshire.

STAFFORDSHIRE

CHEDDLETON
Flint Mill, Leek Road
Open Saturday and Sunday.

A pair of watermills, one of which ground flints for the Staffordshire potteries. Flint pebbles and the finely ground powdered flint were delivered by narrowboats on the nearby Caldon Canal, and at the mill's wharf lies the fully restored Fellows Morton & Clayton horse-drawn narrowboat *Vienna*, built in 1911.

SHUGBOROUGH
Staffordshire County Museum and Mansion House, Shugborough Hall, near Stafford (telephone: Little Haywood 388).
Open mid March to mid October, Tuesday to Friday 10.30 — 5.30, Saturday 2 — 5.30, Sunday 2 — 6.30; mid October to mid March by appointment only.

A splendid eighteenth-century mansion housing many relics of the famous Admiral Anson (1687-1762). The adjoining stable block houses the excellent Staffordshire County Museum.

SUFFOLK

IPSWICH
Pinmill, on the south bank of the river Orwell, 6 miles east of Ipswich, just off the A138
A favourite mooring place for privately preserved Thames barges and gaff-rigged yachts and fishing craft.

LOWESTOFT
Maritime Museum, Sparrows Nest, Whapload Road
Open daily May to October.

This little cottage built of flint beach pebbles is crammed with a fascinating collection of models, paintings, photographs and relics. They are mainly connected with the important local fishing fleet and shipbuilding yards. A most unusual exhibit is a model of a local sailing trawler, powered by a hidden clockwork motor, which bucks and tosses on a sea of painted canvas.

Lowestoft is still a fishing port and on the south side of Lake Lothing, which forms the inner harbour, lie the rotting remains of several fishing smacks. One enterprising amateur boatbuilder has built a full-size replica of one of these sailing trawlers.

SOUTHWOLD
Southwold Museum, St Bartholomews Green (telephone: Southwold 3536)
Open (summer only) Tuesday, Wednesday and Friday 2.30 — 4.30. Other times by appointment.

A museum of local history including some items of shipping interest. There are also a number of ship's figureheads mounted on the street corners of this quaint old seaport town, and on the promenade the Fishermen's Reading Room contains some excellent sailing-ship models, including one of the last local beach yawl, the *Bittern*.

SUDBURY
River Stour Lighter, Sudbury Basin
Details from Miss D. Barratt, 27 The Crescent, Frinton on Sea, Essex.

This vessel was excavated in 1972 by the River Stour Trust and is now being restored. She is a heavy clinker-built craft similar in design to the lighters of the Fens and those painted by Constable, whose landscapes included many views of the Stour and its barges. The Stour was made navigable from its estuary as far as Sudbury in the early eighteenth century, and the last pair of lighters was abandoned in 1928. The Trust hopes to restore the river to navigation.

TYNE AND WEAR
NEWCASTLE UPON TYNE
Science Museum, Exhibition Park (telephone: Newcastle upon Tyne 815129)
Open weekdays October to March 10 — 4.30, April to September 10 — 6; Sunday October to March 1.30 — 4.30, April to September 2 — 5.

The museum was opened in 1934 in a 'temporary' exhibition pavilion and is now crowded with over eight thousand exhibits, many of which are of nautical interest. It is planned to move many of the exhibits for display in the former Cooperative warehouse at West Blandford Street.

The Tyne is still one of the main shipbuilding rivers in Britain and many of the products of its shipyards are represented here as models. The *Mauretania* was probably the best-known ship launched on the Tyne. She was built in 1906 at Swan Hunter's yard for the Cunard Line, the first of a new generation of large express liners, and was intended to place her owners in the forefront of the very competitive transatlantic passenger trade. She could carry 2,300 passengers. Her steam turbines, producing 70,000 shaft horsepower (52,199kW), gave her a speed of up to 26 knots (48km/hour), and she held the blue riband for the fastest crossings of the Atlantic for twenty-two years. Her model, which is very detailed, gives an excellent impression of the beauty of the original ship with her knife-like straight bows and four giant funnels.

The building of the *Mauretania* would not have been possible but for a Tyneside inventor, Charles Parsons, and his experimental launch, the *Turbinia* — the first turbine-powered ship. She was first tested in 1894, but her success was not immediate since there were teething troubles with both propellers and turbines. But all the major problems were overcome in the short space of three years, a remarkable feat of experimental engineering. Final tests in 1897 proved the *Turbinia* to be the fastest, most powerful vessel for her size in the world. She made a spectacular appearance in 1897 at Queen Victoria's jubilee naval review, where she astonished everyone by her speed, which reached a maximum of 34½ knots (64km/hour). Within ten years marine steam turbines came increasingly into use for high-speed naval ships and commercial passenger vessels, eventually achieving a dominance that lasted till modern times.

Paddle tugs were another Tyneside speciality and many were equipped with side-lever engines, which were the most successful of all early types of marine steam engine. Long after they had gone out of use for other types of vessel they continued to be built for paddle tugs because of their simplicity and reliability. The engines of the tug *Lingdale* of 1882 are on show here, along with a model of the paddle tug *Messenger*. The paddle tug *Reliant*, preserved at the National Maritime Museum, was another Tyneside product, as was the *Eppleton Hall*, which in her old age steamed out to the San Francisco Maritime Museum.

The Newcastle museum also has some other local craft under its care. These are three different types of coble. Cobles are clinker-built open boats which have evolved distinct characteristics over the centuries to fit them for local conditions; the *Glad Tidings* is a typical beach boat, with a square transom, twin keels, high bow and deep forefoot. When under way she carried a single lugsail and a rudder projecting some 4 feet (1.2m) below the keel, to act partly as a centreboard. The *Blossom* is a larger type of coble known as a 'mule' and is 33 feet (10.1m) long and double-ended. She was built in 1887 at Berwick, the most northerly port to use cobles. The *Peggy* is a Sunderland foyboat, used for securing and releasing the mooring hawsers of ships in the river. Small cobles like the *Peggy* regularly sailed as far south as the river Tees, then were towed back alongside the incoming ships to moor them for a 'foy' of ten shillings.

The museum is also responsible for the last Tyne wherry, *Elswick II*, which is kept afloat on the river for the present. The clinker-built wherry and the keel, which was carvel-built, were the local types of barge once used to carry coal from the upriver collieries to sea-going colliers moored in the lower section of the river below Newcastle. The *Elswick II*, which measures some 50 feet (15.2m) in overall length, was built in the late 1930s. She and the *Blossom* and the *Peggy* all belong to the Maritime Trust.

SOUTH SHIELDS
Museum and Art Gallery, Ocean Road (telephone: South Shields 68740)
Open weekdays 10 — 6, Sunday 2 — 5.
There are displays on the history of this part of the mouth of the Tyne and its role in the history of lifeboats and lifesaving. An early nineteenth-century lifeboat is preserved on the promenade.

SUNDERLAND
Museum and Art Gallery, Borough Road (telephone: Sunderland 41235)
Open weekdays 9.30 —6, Saturday 9.30 — 4, Sunday 3 — 5.
An important collection of builders' models mainly from local shipyards, including local designs such as the 'turret steamers' designed at Doxford's Yard at the end of the nineteenth century.

WEST MIDLANDS
DUDLEY
Black Country Museum, Tipton Road (telephone: 021-557 9043)
Not yet open except by appointment on Sundays 2 — 5 (summer only).
An ambitious open-air museum of the social and industrial history of the area, still in its early stages. As canals played a major part in the development of industry, there is an important collection of canal material including boats, a working boatyard and a re-erected canal bridge.

WEST SUSSEX
SHOREHAM
Marlipins Museum, High Street
Open Easter, and May to October daily 10 — 12.30, 2 — 5.
The building dates from the twelfth century, and ship models of vessels connected with this coastal port are among its collection.

WORTHING
Worthing Museum and Art Gallery, Chapel Road (telephone: Worthing 204226)
Open weekdays 10 — 7 (October to March 10 — 5).
Some eight to ten ship models are on show, including one of a sailing frigate built by William Hutchens of Devonport Dockyard about 1830/40 and a bone French prisoner-of-war model. There

are also naval relics from a local family, the Hargoods, including Admiral Hargood's Trafalgar Medal.

WEST YORKSHIRE

DEWSBURY
Canal Museum, Saville Town Wharf, Mill Street East (telephone: Dewsbury 46796)
Open Saturdays and Sundays, other times by prior arrangement.

A young museum established and run by the enthusiastic volunteers of the Calder Navigation Society. It is housed in a former blacksmith's shop and stables of the Aire and Calder Navigation, alongside the canal basin. The collection covers two hundred years of waterway history with many original objects, as well as models, paintings and photographs. It is planned to extend the displays to include large outdoor exhibits such as lock-working equipment and canal boats.

Isle of Man

CASTLETOWN
Nautical Museum, Bridge Street (telephone: Douglas 5522)
Open mid May to late September, weekdays 10 — 1, 2 — 5, Sunday 2 — 5.

The museum has been set up in the home of the Quayle family and contains many of their relics. The most important is the little schooner *Peggy*. She was built by the Quayles in 1791, partly as a working boat for collecting goods and passengers from the mainland, and partly as a yacht. She is 25 feet (7.6m) long and is clinker-built. In 1796 she was taken by her owner to race on Windermere. She and another Isle of Man boat were transported by land from Penny Bridge near Ulverston to the south end of Windermere. The *Peggy* was kept in a boat dock under the Quayles' house. She lay here virtually forgotten until the 1930s. She is a rare example of an eighteenth-century open sailing boat. The rest of the house contains excellent displays about the fishing industry of the island and its ships. There is also a sailmaker's loft. Above the *Peggy's* dock, George Quayle built a room to resemble the stern cabin of a large sailing ship, with curved ceiling and stern windows. The lockers in front of the windows contained a secret entrance to the dock below.

DOUGLAS
Manx Museum (telephone: Douglas 5522)
Open weekdays 10 — 5.

The Viking Gallery includes the finds from the two ship burials discovered on the island at Knock-y-Doonee and Balladoole.

Northern Ireland

COUNTY ANTRIM

BELFAST
HMS Caroline, Milewater Basin
Not open to the public.

Possibly the only First World War Royal Navy cruiser still afloat and one of the oldest vessels flying the White Ensign, HMS *Caroline* has served as a Royal Navy Reserve depot ship since 1922.

She was laid down by Cammell Laird at Birkenhead in January and commissioned in December 1914. She was a light cruiser of 3750 tons (3810t) and 40,000 shaft horsepower (29,828kW) with a speed of 29 knots (54km/hour). She was armed with 2 by 6inch (50 by 152mm) guns, 8 by 4inch (203 by 102mm) quick-firing guns and a 3-inch (76mm) anti-aircraft gun.

On commissioning she joined the First Light Cruiser Squadron and took part in many sweeps across the North Sea. In 1916 she lead the Fourth Cruiser Squadron at the battle of Jutland. For the rest of the war she was involved in convoy duties and more patrols in the North Sea. At the end of the war *Caroline* saw service in the East Indies before being paid off in 1922.

For her new role as a depot ship she underwent extensive alterations, including the removal of her armament, boilers and machinery. During the Second World War she became a training ship and depot for armed trawlers. Most divisions of the RNR have been moved from their floating bases to 'stone frigates' ashore, but HMS *Caroline* has so far passed her five-yearly surveys and there is no threat to this historic warship yet.

Ulster Museum, Botanic Gardens (telephone: Belfast 668251)
Open weekdays 11 — 6, Sunday 2.30 — 5.30.

The treasures recovered from the Spanish Armada ship *Girona* are displayed here. She was one of four galleasses — rowing and sailing vessels — of the Naples Squadron. She was wrecked on Lacada Point, County Antrim, while returning to Spain. The site of the wreck was rediscovered in 1967 by the Belgian archaeologist Robert Stenuit and excavated, yielding a rich haul of gold coins, jewellery, guns and navigational equipment.

COUNTY DOWN

HOLYWOOD
Ulster Folk and Transport Museum, Cultra Manor (telephone: Holywood 5411)
Open May to September, weekdays 11 — 7, Sunday 2 — 7 (May to June, Tuesday and Wednesday 11 — 9); October to April, weekdays 11 — 5, Sunday 2 — 5.

The maritime section of this folk museum is a new development and so far only the first stage of an ambitious exhibition plan has been opened. This is a display on iron and steel shipbuilding at Belfast which includes models and pictures of the products of Harland and Wolff's yard such as the first White Star liner, *Oceanic* (1871). Future galleries will illustrate the development of Irish marine transport and fisheries and will display models at present in store or at the Belfast Transport Museum, Witham Street, Belfast. The most exciting part of the project is the display of the large vessels on the museum's stretch of coastline on the shore of the Belfast Lough.

The museum has a collection of over twenty different types of Irish vessel. The three-masted topsail schooner *Result* is the largest. She was built by Paul Rogers in 1893 at Carrickfergus to the design of Richard Ashburner of Barrow, her owner. She was designed to sail fast, to sail without ballast and to be of shallow draught, and she was built of steel to the highest stan-dards. Perhaps as a result of the cost of her building her builder went bankrupt before her launch. Once in service she proved to be fast and handy. In 1909 the Ashburners sold their fleet and she was acquired by Mr H. G. G. Clarke of Braunton, north Devon. During the First World War she was used as a decoy or Q ship with a hidden gun to attack German submarines. She was also fitted with an auxiliary engine and her lofty rig was gradually reduced. After the Second World War a much more powerful engine was fitted and she was cut down to a motor ketch with auxiliary sails, trading until 1967. There is still much work to do before her restoration is complete. At present she is tied up in Belfast docks.

Another boat in the collection is a 52½ foot (16m) 'nickey' which saw ninety-six years of working life before being acquired by the museum in 1973. Built as a two-masted lugger for herring and mackerel fishing, she was first motorised after the First World War with an 18-horsepower (13.4kW) diesel; the propeller was fitted on the port side to prevent the nets worked on the starboard side from fouling it. The *Mary Joseph* was built at Kilkeel, County Down, in 1877 by William Paynter of Cornwall, who had set up a yard there the year before.

The museum also possesses a hooker from Connemara and a wide variety of open boats both from the coast and from the lakes of Ireland. One of the most interesting of these is the *Carpathia*, a fishing boat built at Groomsport in 1912 and named after the Cunard liner which rescued the survivors of the *Titanic*. With her double-ended 34-foot (10.4m) hull and clinker construction, the *Carpathia* is in the same boatbuilding tradition as many open working boats of the north and east coasts of Ireland and has direct connections with the Viking longships of the ninth century.

As she was the first boat at Groomsport to be built with an engine (a 7-horsepower (5.2kW) petrol/paraffin single-cylinder Kalvin) she also represents the early twentieth-century transition from sail and oar to motor propulsion.

Scotland

FIFE

ANSTRUTHER

North Carr Lightship, The Harbour (telephone: Anstruther 310628)
Open April to 31st October, 10 to dusk.

Stationed to guard the dangerous Carr Rocks off Fife Ness, this lightship was withdrawn after forty-two years service and converted into a floating museum, but still with all her original equipment.

Scottish Fisheries Museum, St Ayles, Harbourhead (telephone: Anstruther 310628)
Open April to October, weekdays 10 — 12.30, 2 — 6, Sunday 2 — 5; November to March, daily 2.30 — 4.30 (except Tuesday).

This museum covers the history of the Scottish fishing industry and its fisherfolk, with particular emphasis on the east coast. It is housed in an attractive range of stone buildings grouped round a courtyard and overlooking the harbour with its modern fishing vessels. Two 16-foot (4.9m) open fishing boats, nets and other fishing gear are on show in the courtyard at the entrance to the museum, and inside there are seven galleries and an aquarium. There is an excellent display of models of the many different types of Scottish boats from small sailing craft to modern diesel-powered seine netters. A striking exhibit is the mock-up of a fishing boat's wheelhouse with all the electronic equipment — echo sounders, etc — found on a modern fishing vessel. The attendants are retired fishermen who are well informed about all the exhibits. In the harbour the museum keeps a 70-foot (21.3m) 'fifie' of about 1901 which is being restored to its original rig and will be opened to the public when this work is finished. The fifie was probably the most common type of Scottish deep-sea fishing boat: they were rigged with a high dipping lugsail forward and a small standing lugsail aft. They had sharp, deep hulls with a vertical stem and stern.

KIRKCALDY

Museum and Art Gallery, War Memorial Grounds (telephone: Kirkcaldy 60732)
Open weekdays 11 — 5.

Ship models of local vessels of this fishing and coal port.

GRAMPIAN

ABERDEEN
Art Gallery and Museum, Schoolhill (telephone: Aberdeen 23942)
Open weekdays 10 — 5, Sunday 2 — 5.

Before it became the centre of the North Sea oil industry, Aberdeen was a noted fishing and whaling port. Its shipbuilders, notably Alexander Hall, built some of the best of the nineteenth-century clipper ships. The museum's collections include models of the steam whaler *Eclipse,* a local steam drifter and Hall's best-known clipper ships.

PETERHEAD
Arbuthnot Museum, St Peter Street (telephone: Peterhead 2554)
Open weekdays 10 — 12, 2 — 5.

A local history museum with a section on whaling in the Arctic, once a flourishing industry of this fishing and oil port.

LOTHIAN

EDINBURGH
Royal Scottish Museum, Chambers Street (telephone: 031-225 7534)
Open weekdays 10 — 5, Sunday 2 — 5.

This national museum possesses some excellent ship models in its technology collection. Probably the rarest is the superbly detailed contemporary model of the Dutch East India Company's ship *D'Bataviase Eeuw,* built in 1719. Many of the models have a Scottish origin and include a large number of Scottish fishing boats (some of which are on loan to the Scottish Fisheries Museum at Anstruther), a model of Leith dockyard in 1830, French prisoner-of-war models from Melrose prison, and ships of the Scottish navy before the union such as the *Great Michael* of 1511.

ORKNEY

STROMNESS
Orkney Natural History Museum, 52 Alfred Street (telephone: Stromness 246)
Open weekdays 11 — 5 (Thursday 11 — 1).

Models of local vessels on display include the North Isles yole *Edith,* the schooner *Lavinia* of 1859, and the first steamer to sail between Orkney and the mainland (1856). Other notable items are two models of lighthouses, a set of model engines for a trawler, and models of Brunel's *Great Eastern* (1858) and the Elder Dempster liner *Abosso* of 1912.

SHETLAND
LERWICK
Zetland County Museum
No details of opening times.

Models of local fishing boats and also finds from some seventeenth- and eighteenth-century shipwrecks. The museum also owns the last surviving sixern. Sixerns were large double-ended clinker-built open boats, usually with an overall length of about 37 feet (11.3m), rowed with six oars (and also sailed with a single lugsail), and used for deep-sea line fishing. Although greatly modified in design, they owe their origin to the Viking ships of Scandinavia.

STRATHCLYDE
GLASGOW
Carrick (formerly City of Adelaide), Custom House Quay
Not open to the public.

A former composite clipper (wood planking on iron frames) built at Sunderland in 1864 for Devitt & Moore's cargo and passenger service from London to Australia and still afloat as a club ship, though disguised under an awning roof.

Museum of Transport, 25 Albert Drive (telephone: 041-423 8000)
Open weekdays 10 — 5, Sunday 2 — 5.

This famous collection, which is one of the finest anywhere in the world, has recently been transferred from the Art Gallery and Museum, Kelvingrove, to the new Clyde Room of the Museum of Transport. Some two hundred of the finest models from a collection of almost seven hundred are on show. They reflect Clydeside's expertise in shipbuilding over the past two hundred years.

The shipyards of the river Clyde first came to prominence in the early nineteenth century because of their work in developing steam engines for marine propulsion. A landmark in this field was the construction of the paddle steamer *Comet* by John Wood in 1811-12, the first practical passenger steamer in Europe; she is represented by a model in the display. In 1840 Robert Napier launched the first transatlantic paddle steamer, the *Britannia,* for the British and North American Steam Navigation Company, which was later to become the Cunard Line, and since then many Cunard liners have been built on the Clyde. They are represented in the collection by builders' half-models of the *Abyssinia* (1870), the *Acadia* (1840), sister ship of the *Britannia,* the *Aquitania* (1914), the *Catalonia* (1881), the *China* (1862), the *Scotia* (1862), the *Umbria* (1884), and a spectacularly large and detailed model of the *Queen Mary,* launched from John Brown's yard in 1936. There are many models of passenger liners of other famous companies, including the Inman liner *City of Rome* of 1881, the Canadian Pacific liner *Empress of Scotland* of 1930 and the Union Castle liner *Stirling Castle* of 1936.

The Clyde shipbuilders have built and are continuing to build warships both for the Royal Navy and for foreign navies, and they have donated many warship models to the museum. There are two battleships — *Colossus,* a 'Dreadnought' type of 1909, and *Howe,* 'King George IV' class of 1937-42 — and two battle cruisers — *Indomitable* of 1908 and *Hood* of 1916-20, which was sunk by the German battleship *Bismarck* in 1941 — and a wide range of cruisers, destroyers and anti-submarine patrol vessels and other naval vessels from 1844 to the Second World War. Many of these are built to a scale of 1 to 48 and are full of intriguing detail — some of the finest achievements in the art of the shipyard modelmaker. The most unusual model of all is that of the *Livadia,* which was a unique circular yacht built in 1880 by John Elder & Company for Tsar Alexander II of Russia to the design of Admiral Popoff. She was intended to be both very stable and unsinkable.

This Glasgow collection does not confine itself solely to the products of the Clydeside yards; for example, there is a Navy Board model of HMS *Oxford,* a 54-gun frigate launched at Portsmouth dockyard in 1727. The rigging, which is unusual on this type of model, is complete and mainly original. There are also some good examples of wood and bone French prisoner-of-war models. The museum publishes an illustrated catalogue of its collection in four parts.

Paddle steamer Waverley, Anderston Quay and at many of the piers on the Clyde
Day, afternoon and evening cruises, May to September.

The last sea-going paddle steamer in the world, she was built by A. & J. Inglis on the Clyde in 1947 and in her time has carried thousands of holidaymakers from Glasgow to the resorts of the Clyde estuary. She is 239 feet (72.8m) long and has a service speed of 14 knots (26km/hour). She was originally owned by the London & North Eastern Railway, but with the nationalisation of the railways at the end of 1947 she came under the ownership of the Caledonian Steam Packet Company. She continued her summer excursions until 1973, when she was laid up. The following year the Waverley Steam Navigation Company was set up by paddle-steamer enthusiasts to restore and run her as a tourist attraction. After strenuous efforts to raise funds for her refit, many gifts of materials from commercial firms and thousands of hours of volunteer labour, she was put back into passenger service in May 1975 and carried over 120,000 passengers. However, her future was still not assured because of the withdrawal of a subsidy from the local regional council. Another public appeal was launched and raised £70,000 to pay for refitting and retubing her boiler, and an agreement was reached with Caledonian-Macbrayne Limited, the rival operators of the veteran screw steamer *Queen Mary*. The 1976 season proved even more successful than 1975. In 1977 she broke new ground by sailing down to Liverpool to run a week of excursions from the Mersey. These proved very popular, as did her later voyages on the Clyde. Unfortunately on 15th July 1977, while attempting to dock at Dunoon Pier, she ran aground. She slid off the rocks nine hours later and in dry-dock it was found she had been holed in four places and twisted 40 feet (12.2m) on her keel. The cost of repairs and the loss of revenue have wiped out all hope of an operating surplus to use for her next refit. The problems of maintaining an old vessel in working condition are immense and very costly, but the *Waverley* has proved a tremendous attraction to holidaymakers and it has been well worth making the effort to keep her steaming.

GREENOCK
McLean Museum, 9 Union Street, West End (telephone: Greenock 23741)
Open October to March, 10 — 12.30, 2 — 4.30; April to September, 10 — 12.30, 2 — 5.
Builders' models of ships launched by the local shipyards.

PAISLEY
Paisley Museum and Art Galleries, High Street (telephone: 041-889 3151)
Open weekdays 10 — 5 (Tuesday 10 — 8, Saturday 10 — 6).
Models of nineteenth-century merchant steamers, dredgers and yachts, mainly the products of Simons and Company, Renfrew (1810-1946).

TAYSIDE
DUNDEE
Barrack Street Museum, Barrack Street (telephone: Dundee 27866, 25492 and 25493)
Open Monday to Friday 10 — 5, Saturday 10 — 1, 2 — 5.
A museum devoted to shipping and for temporary exhibitions. It houses an extensive display of models of locally built ships — from fishing boats to ferries and freighters — navigational instruments and other maritime relics. There is also a Victorian racing skiff once used on the river Tay.

Broughty Castle Museum, Broughty Ferry (telephone: Dundee 76121)
Open weekdays (except Friday) 11 — 1, 2 — 5, Sunday (July to October) 2 — 5.

Among the displays, which include local military and natural history, there is an extensive section on the Dundee whaling industry. This started in the mid eighteenth century but was of little importance until the growth in the nineteenth century of Dundee's jute-spinning mills, which used whale oil in their processes. Dundee shipowners were among the first to use steam vessels, and by the mid 1850s Dundee had outstripped its old rival Hull and become the premier whaling port.

Dundee Museum and Art Galleries, Albert Square (telephone: Dundee 25492 and 25493)
Open weekdays 10 — 5.30.

Local archaeological displays include two dugout canoes, one of which is 29 feet (8.8m) long and was found in Perthshire in 1895. Their date is as yet unknown.

HMS Unicorn, Victoria Dock
Not regularly open to the public as yet; details of open days from the HMS *Unicorn* Preservation Trust, Dundee.

After 1860 virtually all the wooden warships of the Royal Navy were superseded by ships built of iron. However, many were not immediately sent for breaking up and instead were used as floating depot ships, training vessels, reformatories, orphanages and hospitals. Flotillas of these old 'wooden walls', with their masts cut down and a Noah's ark roof over their upper decks, were to be found in all the major ports of the British Isles. They were particularly used as the training ships of local branches of the Royal Naval Reserve. Some survived as late as the 1950s, but they have all been scrapped except for the *Foudroyant* at Portsmouth and the *Unicorn* at Dundee. HMS *Unicorn* was built at Chatham in 1824 as a large and heavily armed frigate of forty-six guns, with a tonnage of just over 1000 tons (1061t). She incorporated all the latest technical developments such as iron brackets (known as knees) and diagonally positioned iron strips to reinforce her side planking. But she was never actually commissioned as a fighting ship, for she spent her whole career, before her arrival at Dundee in 1873, either laid up or as a gunpowder storage hulk. She served as the Royal Naval Reserve ship until she was paid off in the late 1960s. She was drydocked and found to be in very sound condition; the preservation society which cares for her hopes to rig her fully and open her to the general public.

Wales
CLWYD

LLANGOLLEN
Canal Museum, The Wharf
Open Easter to September, 11 — 5.
   A small but well-designed and award-winning museum about the history of the Shropshire Union Canal.

DYFED

HAVERFORDWEST
Pembrokeshire Museum, The Castle Museum and Art Gallery (telephone: Haverfordwest 3708)
Open summer 10 — 5.30, winter 11 — 4.
   A new and developing museum service with an active interest in the archaeological investigation of historic shipwrecks on the Pembrokeshire coast. Displays at present include some excellent photographs of warships being built at the former naval base at Pembroke Dock.

MILFORD HAVEN
HMS Warrior, Llanion Point
Not open to the public.
   HMS *Warrior* was the first iron-built and armoured sea-going warship. She was constructed at Blackwall by the Thames Ironworks in 1859-61. This vessel may be said to have opened the modern era of shipbuilding for war. While the typical warships of the 1850s were unarmoured wooden vessels, liable to easy penetration and destruction by shellfire, this new ship was practically indestructible by contemporary shells and shot. Her side armour was 4½ inches (114mm) thick, backed by 18 inches (457mm) of solid teak — which helps to explain her long career. Her guns were positioned along the sides of her hull in the traditional broadside pattern, and she was fitted with a lifting propeller and full set of sails. In her old age she became an accommodation ship and later an oil fuel jetty. She is still serving in this role but if she is ever paid off she must be a prime candidate for preservation. Unfortunately, very little remains of her original fittings. However, the Science Museum, London, possess an excellent rigged model of her in her original condition.

GWENT

MONMOUTH
Nelson Museum, The Market Hall, Priory Street (telephone: Monmouth 2122)
Open April to October, weekdays 10.30 — 1, 2.15 — 5.15 (July and August 10 — 6), Sundays during July and August 2.30 — 5.30.

The museum contains a collection of objects associated with Admiral Lord Nelson, Lady Hamilton and their contemporaries.

GWYNEDD

BANGOR
Industrial Railway Museum, Penrhyn Castle
Open April, May, October and all Saturdays and Sundays 2 — 5; June to September Monday to Friday 11 — 5.

A nineteenth-century version of a Norman castle financed by a fortune made in slate mining. The Industrial Railway Museum set up in the stables includes builders' half-models and pictures of the steam coasters that carried cargoes of slates from the nearby harbour of Port Dinorwic.

BARMOUTH
Lifeboat Museum, The Quay
Open daily 11 — 1, 2 — 4, 7 — 9; afternoons and evenings on Sunday (summer only).

A little museum in a caravan telling the story of the local lifeboats.

PORTMADOC
Maritime Museum, The Harbour
Opening times not available.

Based on the old coasting ketch *Garlandstone*, which has been restored.

SOUTH GLAMORGAN

CARDIFF
National Museum of Wales (telephone: Cardiff 397951)
Open weekdays April to September 10 — 6, October to March 10 — 5; Sunday 2.30 — 5. Closed on bank holidays, Christmas holidays, New Year's Day and Good Friday.

The Industry Gallery has a large section devoted to Welsh shipping history with some excellent models. There is a striking collection of builders' models of tramp steamers once owned in the coal-exporting ports of South Wales and a comprehensive array of Welsh fishing-boat types. Some of the latter are set in dioramas to illustrate the environment in which the full-size craft sailed. A huge lighthouse lantern with its multiple lenses dominates the displays, which are arranged at two levels in the form of a ship's bridge.

Welsh Industrial and Maritime Museum, Bute Street, Docks, Cardiff (telephone: Cardiff 371805)
Open same times as the National Museum.

The first stage of this new museum displaying many large pieces of machinery for which there was no space in the central building of the National Museum was opened by the Prime Minister, James Callaghan, in April 1977. The first two full-size nautical exhibits are the Bristol Channel pilot cutter *Kindly Light,* a 54-foot (16.5m) cutter built for the Newport pilots at Fleetwood in 1904 and preserved in cooperation with the Maritime Trust, and the steam tug *Sea Alarm,* built as the *Empire Ash* at Sunderland in 1941 and used for towing in the Bristol Channel by C. K. King & Company until 1972. Both vessels have been placed in permanent berths and are still being restored.

ST FAGANS
Welsh Folk Museum (telephone: Cardiff 561357)
Open April to September weekdays, 10 — 6, Sunday 2.30 — 6; October to March, weekdays 10 — 5, Sunday 2.30 — 5.
In the grounds of an Elizabethan mansion, Welsh cottages, farms and mills have been re-erected to form an open-air folk museum. Welsh inshore and river fisheries are well covered, with a display of nets, equipment and boats, including several varieties of coracle.

WEST GLAMORGAN
SWANSEA
Maritime and Industrial Museum, South Dock (telephone: Swansea 50351)
Open weekdays 10.30 — 5.30.
The museum is part of a larger project to renovate the obsolete South Dock and its quays to turn it into a centre for recreation. It is housed in a late Victorian warehouse formerly used by Coast Lines, and the first phase of the museum opened in June 1977.

Glossary

Barque: a vessel of three or more masts square-rigged on all except the aftermost mast, which is fore and aft rigged.
Brig: a vessel with two masts square-rigged on both.
Carvel: a method of shipbuilding in which the planks are placed edge to edge.
Clinker: another method of shipbuilding, where the edges of the planks overlap.
Clipper: a fine-lined ship built for speed, usually referring to nineteenth-century deep-sea sailing ships.
Cutter: a vessel with one mast, fore and aft rigged with more than one jib or headsail.

Deadeyes: round wooden blocks with three holes, used in pairs with a small length of rope (a lanyard) for tightening stays of masts (mainly on old sailing ships).

Fore and aft: referring to a vessel whose sails are spread from spars which are set parallel to the keel (from bow to stern).

Frames: the ribs which give a ship its shape and together with the deck beams maintain it against the pressure of wind and water. Planking or iron or steel plating are secured to the frames.

Gaff: the upper spar holding up a fore and aft sail.

Jib: a triangular fore and aft sail set between the bow or bowsprit and the foremast (the first of the ship).

Keel: the main longitudinal (fore and aft) structural member or backbone of a vessel.

Ketch: a vessel with two masts, the mizzenmast being smaller than the mainmast and positioned in front of the rudder.

Lateen: a triangular sail set on a spar. It first appeared in the Mediterranean in the early middle ages and is common on Arab sailing vessels.

Leeboards: pivoted boards fitted on the sides of flat-bottomed boats as a substitute for a keel, to prevent drifting to leeward.

Lugsail (lugger): a quadrilateral fore and aft sail with its head (i.e. top edge) attached to a yard. A boat so equipped is known as a lugger.

Mizzen: the third mast of a three-masted vessel (from the bow, i.e., fore, main, mizzen, and if more than three, jigger, driver and spanker).

Schooner: a vessel with fore and aft sails on two or more masts.

Ship: a vessel with three or more masts, all square-rigged.

Shrouds: the stays of a mast attached on either side of the vessel.

Sloop: a single-masted, fore and aft rigged vessel with one jib.

Spritsail: a fore-aft sail, set on a diagonal spar or sprit, e.g. Thames barges.

Square-rigged: a vessel whose sails are spread from yards at ninety degrees to the keel.

Stay: a rope supporting a mast (see also *Shrouds*).

Topsail: the sail set above the lowest sail of a square-rigged vessel, or above the mainsail of a fore and aft rigged vessel.

Transom: a square stern.

Turbine: an engine driven by steam or gas impinging on vanes or blades, some of which are fixed, while others are attached to a moving rotor to which the output shaft is coupled.

Yard: a spar supporting and extending a square sail.

Useful books and periodicals

British Fishing Boats and Inshore Craft. R. W. White. Science Museum (HMSO), 1957.

Catalogue of Glasgow Museum's Shipping Collection (in four parts). Glasgow Museum.

The Development of the Boat, A Select Bibliography. National Maritime Museum (HMSO).

The Iron Ship. Dr E. W. Corlett. Moonraker Press, 1976.

John Harrison and his Chronometers. R. T. Gould. National Maritime Museum (HMSO).

The Merchant Sailing Ship, A Photographic History. B. Greenhill and A. Giffard. David & Charles.

Old Order, New Thing. H. Campbell MacMurray. National Maritime Museum (HMSO). (On the tug *Reliant.*)

Sailing Ships, Their History and Development. G. S. Laird Clowes. Science Museum (HMSO), 1959

Mariner's Mirror (quarterly). Society for Nautical Research, c/o National Maritime Museum.

Maritime Wales (annually). Gwynedd Archives Service, Caernarvon.

Sea Breezes (monthly magazine). The Journal of Commerce, Water Street, Liverpool 2.

Yearbook of the Ulster Folk and Transport Museum.

Useful addresses

The Business Archives Council, 64 Queen Victoria Street, London EC4.

The Council for Nautical Archaeology, c/o The Institute of Archaeology, University of London, 31/34 Gordon Square, London WC1. Telephone: 01-387 6052.

The Inland Waterways Association, 114 Regents Park Road, London NW1. Telephone: 01-586 2556.

The Institute of Marine Engineers, 76 Mark Lane, London EC3.

The Maritime Trust, 16 Ebury Street, London W1Y 1FH. Telephone: 01-730 0096.

The Museums Association, 87 Charlotte Street, London W1P 2BX. Telephone: 01-636 4600.

The Society for Nautical Research, c/o The National Maritime Museum, Greenwich, London SE10 9NF.

The Standing Conference for Local History, 26 Bedford Square, London WC1. Telephone: 01-636 4066.

The World Ship Society, Dept. SB, 10 Brockhampton Road, Havant, Hampshire.

Index

INDEX